A FLORA OF
TIREE, GUNNA AND COLL

D. A. Pearman & C. D. Preston

DORCHESTER

2000

Privately published by D. A. Pearman and C. D. Preston

with the support of
the Glasgow Natural History Society
and
Scottish Natural Heritage

Obtainable from Mrs A. V. Pearman, The Old Rectory,
Frome St Quintin, Dorchester, Dorset DT2 0HF.

Cover photo: Yellow Flag (*Iris pseudacorus*), RSPB reserve, Coll,
June 1995. Photographed by C.H. Gomersall/RSPB-Images.

Printed by Cigam Group, Newcastle-upon-Tyne, England

ISBN 0-9538111-1-5

DEDICATED TO MRS JOAN CLARK

(1908–1999)

AN INDOMITABLE BOTANIST AND A GOOD FRIEND TO OTHERS
BOTANISING ON THE ISLANDS

HER WORK PROVIDES THE BASIS FOR THIS FLORA

CONTENTS

LIST OF FIGURES

LIST OF TABLES

FOREWORD

The western islands of Tiree, Coll and Gunna, famous for their long hours of sunshine and yet very different in their habitats, have long held a fascination for travellers, especially those interested in wildlife, landscapes and colour. Botanists are no exception and this volume is the result of records begun in 1819 stretching through to 1999. It was Joan Clark, BSBI vice-county recorder in the 1980s, who first started a card index of the islands' flora. She was followed by Agnes Walker, and very recently, by myself. Agnes was encouraged by Joan to begin a checklist, which was taken forward actively as a full flora by David Pearman and Chris Preston in 1996. The flora is full of information about the distribution and occurrence of all the higher plant species found on the islands, and is aimed at making that available for the informed botanist and conservationist, and those who wish to become better acquainted with the attractive plants. I know that visitors often ask the locals about the various plants they see – this will help answer some of those questions. I hope, in the next few years, to complement this book with an illustrated guide to the common and special plants. In the meantime I commend this volume to you, and hope you will use and enjoy it.

Lynne Farrell
Botanical Society of the British Isles Vice-county recorder for Mull, Coll and Tiree
December 1999

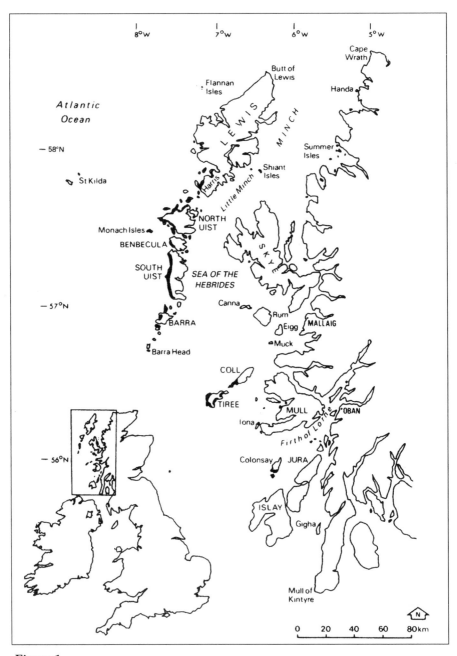

Figure 1

Location of Tiree and Coll (adapted from maps in Boyd & Boyd 1990).
The heavy black lines denote areas of machair.

INTRODUCTION

Tiree and Coll are a contrasting pair of oceanic islands. Tiree is utterly treeless and very nearly flat, with probably the most intact crofting community in the Hebrides, thanks in no small measure to the fertility conferred by the sand blown over the whole island. Coll has some machair but more moorland and is more undulating and acidic. Wind and sunshine are our dominant memories of both islands.

The first detailed account of the Tiree flora was published by Macvicar (1898); forty years later Heslop Harrison *et al.* (1941) prepared a flora of all three islands, Tiree, Gunna and Coll. The islands are therefore relatively well-recorded, and offer an opportunity to assess the effects on the flora of a century which has been marked by considerable economic and agricultural change.

Our account of the flora draws on an extensive amount of fieldwork which has taken place since 1941. Four extended visits have been made by Botanical Society of the British Isles (BSBI) parties, and a comprehensive card index was compiled by Mrs Joan Clark, the BSBI vice-county recorder from 1979 to 1989. This index and the subsequent work of Mrs Clark and her successor Dr Agnes Walker formed the inspiration for this flora.

On the BSBI meetings of 1989 and 1990, some members of the party undertook to study particular aspects of the flora and vegetation in more detail. Studies of the saltmarshes, standing waters and charophytes (stone-worts) will be published in detail elsewhere (Leach in press, Preston *et al.* in press, Stewart & Preston in press), although a summary of the distribution of the charophytes is included here. A fourth study, the distribution of Cyperaceae on Tiree, is included in this book.

LOCATION

Tiree, Gunna and Coll are the most westerly islands of the Inner Hebrides (Fig. 1). They are aligned along an axis running from south-west to north-east. Tiree and Coll are separated by a rocky sound, not more than half a mile wide, in which the small island of Gunna lies. Both Tiree and Coll are about twelve miles long, and three to four miles wide. Our islands are about seven miles west of Mull, and are included with that island, and other small islets, in Watsonian vice-county 103, Mid Ebudes.

Heslop Harrison made a strong plea that Tiree, Coll and Gunna had little affinity with Mull, but corresponded much more closely with the Outer Hebrides (v.c. 110), thirty miles or more to the north-west (Heslop Harrison 1941a, Heslop Harrison *et al.* 1941). He proposed that our islands be redesignated v.c. 110B. This suggestion was ruthlessly dealt with by A. J. Wilmott

(1944) who in countering "this unintentionally subversive tendency" (for emendation) stressed that the value of the vice-county system was dependent upon the absolute permanence of the boundaries, and that the original boundaries were known to be entirely arbitrary, so there was no point whatsoever in trying to make this or that boundary a natural one.

TOPOGRAPHY

Madders & Moser (1989) calculate the length of the coastline of Tiree as 67.6 km and that of Coll as 64.9 km. Tiree is flat. Its highest point, Ben Hynish, is 141 m above sea-level, but apart from this hill, and Ceann a'Mhara and Beinn Hough, very little land is above 10 m, and the island stretches out as a plain with few distinguishing features. Gunna reaches only 36 m, whilst Coll, flat in the west other than at Ben Feall (66 m), is much more hummocky in the centre and east although the highest point is still only 104 m at Ben Hogh. For a map of the islands showing the main localities, see Fig. 2.

Tiree has around 37 named lochs including two substantial water bodies in the west, L. a'Phuill and L. Bhasapol. Coll has 40 named lochs; the largest are in the centre of the island but these are not the most interesting botanically. On both islands there are numerous standing waters marked but not named on the 1:25 000 maps, ranging from lochs of moderate size to tiny pools. According to our counts, there are 96 such waters above the high-water mark on Tiree and 64 on Coll (excluding wells and springs). There are many small burns running down to the sea on both islands but few of any size or significance; the major exception is An Fhaodhail, the stream flowing through The Reef on Tiree. Gunna lacks both standing waters and large burns, although there are a few small burns, splash pools and flushes on the island.

CLIMATE

"The Hebrides share with Shetland and Faeroes the distinction of having the most maritime climate in Europe. This characteristic is approached but not surpassed by the outer coasts of Norway, southern Iceland, Ireland and north-west Spain." (Green & Harding 1983). The climate of the Hebrides is relatively uniform, with only small differences between summer and winter temperatures and a restricted diurnal range. Frost is uncommon in winter at low altitudes and virtually unknown in summer; snowfall is rare. Rainfall is high, though not quite so high as the wettest areas on the mainland of north-west Scotland. Rainfall is highest in winter and least in spring, and tends to fall as prolonged periods of moderate rain rather than in short, very heavy downpours. Mean windspeeds are high and gales frequent. The relative humidity in daytime in summer is significantly higher than that in lowland England, whereas

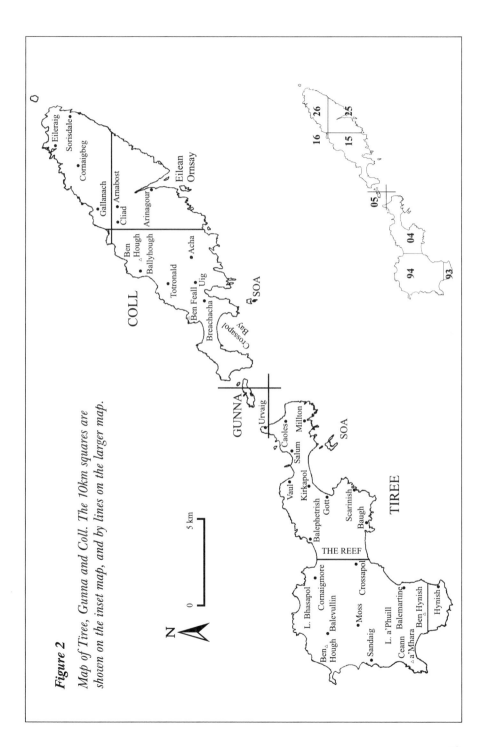

Figure 2

Map of Tiree, Gunna and Coll. The 10km squares are shown on the inset map, and by lines on the larger map.

13

at night and in winter the values are similar to those elsewhere in Britain. The potential water deficit in most areas of the Hebrides is minimal.

Climatic variation within the Hebrides is also discussed by Green & Harding (1983) on the basis of the limited meteorological data available. The position of Coll and Tiree in the open ocean and their low relief are the most important features influencing their climate relative to more sheltered or more mountainous islands. In these features the islands are closer to the Outer Hebrides than to Mull, Rum or Skye. The effect of uninterrupted ocean to the west and the subdued topography is to give Coll and Tiree little shelter from salt-laden winds, a relatively low rainfall and a high sunshine total (because there is nothing to interrupt the passage of rain-bearing air masses). The rainfall of Coll and Tiree is lower than that at sea-level on the more mountainous islands, and much lower than that at higher altitudes on those islands. The sunshine total on Tiree is as high as that in inland England. Consequently potential water deficits are higher on Coll and Tiree than in most areas in the Hebrides. The islands can therefore be expected to offer climatic conditions which are more suitable to southern plant species than the Outer Hebrides, the more montane Inner Hebridean islands or the adjacent mainland.

GEOLOGY AND SOILS

Tiree and Coll are almost entirely comprised of Lewisian Gneiss, a hard, impervious, acid rock which does not break down into a good soil (Darling 1955). There is a small outcrop of marble at Balephetrish on Tiree. Both islands were heavily glaciated, and in the uplift of the land following melting of the ice extensive raised beaches were created – 75% of Tiree is a raised tidal platform (Boyd & Boyd 1990). Hudson & Henderson (1983) map most of the soils on Tiree as 'peaty podsols with peat and peaty gleys', also showing small areas of 'peaty gleys with some peat and peaty podsols'. The proportions are reversed on Coll, where most of the acidic soils are mapped in the peaty gley category.

The acidity and infertility of the islands is considerably ameliorated by machair, extensive accumulations of blown sand which are of very ancient origin (Boyd & Boyd 1990). Indeed one third of Tiree (Mather *et al.* 1975), half of Gunna and at least an eighth of Coll is strongly influenced by calcareous sand deposits (Fig. 3). South Uist, an island renowned for its machair, only has 10% blown sand cover (Ritchie 1976). There are extensive reefs for 20 kilometres to the west of Tiree, and shoals and reefs all around that island. These not only break up the waves, which means that the Tiree coast is not usually exposed to huge storms, but also provide the source of broken shells for the sandy beaches. Coll only has reefs and shallow water off the west coast, but it is sheltered to some extent by Tiree. As shown in Fig. 3, this gives rise to continuous machair land – the machair generated from relatively small areas of beach has coalesced. The large areas of calcareous dunes and machair on Tiree and in western Coll, and smaller areas along the northern coast of Coll, are classified by Hudson & Henderson (1983) as regosols, immature soils developed over unconsolidated parent material. The detailed maps of the beaches of Coll and Tiree and their adjacent areas of dune and machair published by Mather *et al.* (1975) distinguish rocks, shingle, blown sand, machair and some vegetation types.

MAIN HABITATS

The total areas of different habitats on Tiree and Coll are given in Table 1, which has been adapted from Shepherd (1989). We are fortunate that Dargie (1993) has carried out an extensive survey of the vegetation of Tiree, based on the National Vegetation Classification (Rodwell 1991–1995 & in press). The main communities are mentioned below, with their NVC code numbers; the code numbers are listed with their names in Table 2. For full details of these communities, and of less common communities and undescribed variants, Dargie's report must be consulted.

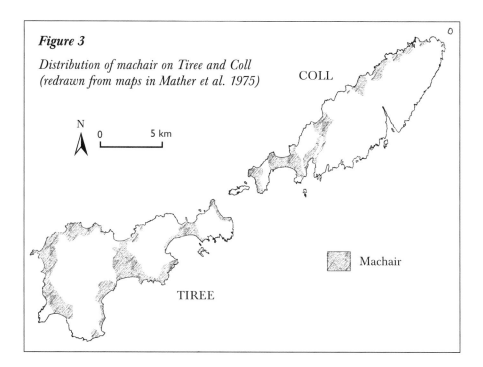

Figure 3

Distribution of machair on Tiree and Coll (redrawn from maps in Mather et al. 1975)

COLL

N

0   5 km

Machair

TIREE

Strand, dunes, machair and saltmarshes

Both main islands, but particularly Tiree, have extensive stretches of sandy beach, with their attendant dunes. On Tiree they are found all around the island, whereas on Coll they are largely confined to the west end, and to the north coast. The sand is principally derived from sea-shells and is therefore calcareous. Blown sand from the beaches forms dunes and then machair. The strandlines, which are often marked by large amounts of cast-up seaweed, support very occasional plants of *Atriplex glabriuscula*, *Cakile maritima* and *Honckenya peploides* (SD2). Other, rarer, plants include *Atriplex laciniata*, *A. praecox* and *Calystegia soldanella*. *Catabrosa aquatica* may be frequent, especially where a burn flows over sandy flats. Most beaches have dunes behind, with *Ammophila arenaria*, *Carex arenaria*, *Elymus farctus*, *Festuca rubra* and *Sonchus arvensis* (SD6 and SD7). *Calystegia soldanella*, *Eryngium maritimum* and *Leymus*

Table 1

The area of different habitats on Tiree and Coll. The table is adapted from Shepherd (1989, table 4.1). Shepherd provides no figures for strands or aquatic habitats, but we have estimated the latter. The area of arable has declined since Shepherd's table was produced.

Habitat	Area in hectares (ha)		
	Tiree	*Coll*	*Total*
Dunes and dry machair	1890	940	2830
Wet machair	145	30	175
Heaths and acid grasslands			
Short heath	1020	240	1260
Deep heath	355	2030	2385
Acidic grassland	610	1690	2300
Blanket Bog	15	950	965
Reed, Iris and Rush beds	420	280	700
Marsh and fen	105	75	180
Old runways	2		2
Arable	150	15	165
Dry pastures	1710	340	2050
Wet pastures	850	435	1285
Agriculturally improved			
pastures	215	5	220
Aquatic	213	370	583
Total	**7700**	**7400**	**15,100**

---

arenaria are rare species which occur with these dominants. The moss *Tortula ruraliformis* often forms patches in these dunes.

The machair, a Gaelic word which describes pasture on soil which is predominantly shell sand (Ritchie 1976), lies behind the dunes and is dominated by *Festuca rubra* and *Galium verum* var. *maritimum* (SD8), with a wealth of colourful perennials including *Bellis perennis, Campanula rotundifolia, Geranium sanguineum, Ranunculus acris, Rhinanthus minor, Saxifraga hypnoides, Thalictrum minus, Thymus polytrichus* and many orchids, especially *Coeloglossum viride* and *Dactylorhiza fuchsii.* In the wetter areas, the slacks, which are not particularly extensive, *Hydrocotyle vulgaris,* with *Carex nigra, Potentilla anserina* and *Ranunculus flammula* (SD17) are the most frequent species, with occasional *Ophioglossum vulgatum* and *Salix repens.*

Because of the strength of the winds blowing the sand, some of the machairs occur well inland. The richest and most extensive is The Reef, on Tiree, which stretches across the whole island from north to south grading from dry, in the south and west, where part is occupied by the airport, to wet in the north and east, along the edge of the stream, An Fhaodhail. This machair is traditionally let for winter and spring grazing (1st November to 31st May) for 199 cows and their followers. It is a spectacular site in summer, with many orchids and substantial populations of *Juncus balticus.* Other notable plants on The Reef include *Dactylorhiza traunsteineri* and *Ophioglossum azoricum.* Surveys of the vegetation, in addition to that of Dargie (1993), have been carried out by Cadbury (1996) and Cadbury & Cowie (1998).

Other seaside communities include shingle beaches and saltmarshes. Shingle beaches are relatively uncommon and support very little vegetation apart from *Galium aparine* and *Matricaria maritima* (SD3). *Mertensia maritima* currently occurs in only two places on Tiree, one supporting a sizeable colony and the other a single plant.

Saltmarshes too are small, uncommon and fragmentary. They often occur only as patches amongst rocks, particularly on coasts with eastern exposure, and are dominated by *Festuca rubra,* with *Carex flacca, Glaux maritima* and *Juncus gerardii* (SM16). Other species include *Bolboschoenus maritimus, Carex distans, C. extensa, C. otrubae* and *Schoenoplectus tabernaemontani,* with rarer *Ruppia maritima* and *Blysmus rufus. Puccinellia maritima* with *Plantago maritima* and *Armeria maritima* (SM13) also occurs frequently. There was a small saltmarsh at the mouth of An Fhaodhail, but this has largely disappeared since a tidal flap valve was fitted there in 1977. For a detailed description of the saltmarsh communities see Leach (in press).

Heaths and acid grasslands

Heaths occur in the interior of Tiree, especially around the higher areas in the west, by Ceann a'Mhara, Ben Hynish and near Balephetrish, but in small

17

patches in many other places. On Coll they are much more extensive, forming mosaics with mires and lochans over all the island away from areas of blown sand. The most frequent dry community is dominated by *Calluna vulgaris* and *Erica cinerea* (H10), usually in conjunction with wet heath comprising *Erica tetralix* and *Trichophorum cespitosum* (M15). The latter type is probably the most common community on Tiree and Coll. Dargie (1993) states that the dry heaths are being rapidly converted by grazing into acid grasslands, specially those with *Calluna vulgaris, Danthonia decumbens, Galium saxatile* and *Nardus stricta* (U5). Grasslands with *Agrostis capillaris* and *Festuca ovina* (U4) may also be increasing due to grazing pressure. Other frequent plants in the drier areas are *Carex binervis* and *C. pilulifera*, often with *Anthoxanthum odoratum, Festuca vivipara* and *Succisa pratensis*. Shallow soils around rock outcrops have *Antennaria dioica* and *Pilosella officinarum* and on Coll *Arctostaphylos uva-ursi* and *Juniperus communis* may be found in clefts in the rocks. In the wetter areas *Carex panicea, Empetrum nigrum* and *Vaccinium myrtillus* occur, but the last two are more or less confined to Coll. On Tiree there is little *Pteridium aquilinum*, and *Ulex europaeus* is confined to sites where it has been planted.

Mires

On Tiree mire communities cover large areas, and as mentioned above, *Trichophorum cespitosum – Erica tetralix* wet heath (M15) is probably the most common vegetation community. On Coll, mire communities are even more widespread. Common components of this vegetation include *Eriophorum angustifolium, Narthecium ossifragum, Potentilla erecta* and a wealth of *Carex* species, particularly *C. echinata, C. nigra, C. panicea* and *C. viridula*. Notable is the frequency of *Schoenus nigricans*, probably because of the influence of salt-spray, with *Carex dioica, C. pulicaris* and *Eleocharis quinqueflora*.

On Coll there are small areas of blanket mire, with *Trichophorum cespitosum* and *Eriophorum vaginatum* (M 17) with many of the species listed above together with *Myrica gale* and more frequent *Molinia caerulea*, and pockets of *Molinia caerulea – Potentilla erecta* mire (M 25).

On both islands there is much rush-pasture, consisting of *Juncus effusus* and *J. acutiflorus*, with *Galium palustre, Holcus lanatus* and other species mentioned above (M 23).

Cliffs and gorges

Most sea cliffs have extensive swards of *Festuca rubra* with *Plantago* species (MC10) or with *Armeria maritima* (MC8). In places, but especially on Coll, heathy vegetation, with low *Scilla verna* and *Calluna vulgaris* heath, extends to the edges of the cliffs. Here and there *Asplenium marinum* and dwarfed

Polypodium vulgare are found in rock crevices with *Ligusticum scoticum* (MC 2).

The great north-facing cliff of Ceann a'Mhara, Tiree, holds species intolerant of grazing including *Alchemilla glabra*, *Hyacinthoides non-scripta*, *Sedum rosea* and *Silene dioica*. *Astragalus danicus* occurs here too. Ben Feall on Coll, and some of the gorges on that island, hold some of these species but never as many.

Coll has many small gorges with woody species, although recent records are sparse (probably from lack of recording rather than disappearance of species through fires or grazing). Trees and shrubs in these gorges include *Alnus glutinosa*, *Betula pubescens*, *Corylus avellana*, *Sorbus aucuparia* and species of *Rosa*, *Rubus* and *Salix*. These occur with herbs such as *Hyacinthoides non-scripta*, *Oxalis acetosella* and *Teucrium scorodonia* and many ferns. These woody species are entirely or virtually absent from Tiree.

Woodland

The treelessness of the islands has long been a feature which visitors have remarked upon. Tiree has nothing which even approaches natural woodland. The nearest to a surviving woodland that we have seen on Coll is west of Caolas-an-eilean (grid ref. NM 219556), where there are thickets of *Populus tremula* and *Sorbus aucuparia* with *Salix cinerea* nearby. Plantations, especially at Arinagour, provide small areas of mature woodland, and include planted tree species such as *Acer pseudoplatanus*, *Alnus glutinosa*, *A. incana*, *Fagus sylvatica*, *Fraxinus excelsior*, *Picea abies*, *P. sitchensis*, *Populus tremula* and *Quercus robur*.

The scarcity of trees on Tiree is so great that the tiny experimental plantation of exotic trees and shrubs by the disused manse at Gott Bay (grid ref. NM 0445) has become well known. The fact that tallest species in this plantation are 'palm trees' (actually *Cordyline australis*) is often drawn to the attention of visitors, and is cited in local guide books as proof of Tiree's mildness. The wind-beaten appearance of the other species persisting here in 1997 (which included *Alnus glutinosa*, *Escallonia macrantha*, *Olearia macrodonta*, *Rosa rugosa*, *Salix* sp. and *Sorbus intermedia*) suggested that tolerance of gale-force winds has been a major reason for its success.

One of the crucial questions facing students of vegetational history in the Hebrides is whether the landscape was more wooded before the onset of human interference, intensive grazing, moor burning and the spread of blanket bog (Birks & Williams 1983). Although we know of no detailed study of the vegetational history of Coll and Tiree, it seems reasonable to assume that it would not have been too dissimilar to that of the Outer Hebrides, which are climatically and ecologically similar. In the Outer Hebrides woodland developed during the early Holocene, and remained in all but the most marginal areas until 4000 years ago. A range of woody species was present, including *Alnus glutinosa*, *Corylus avellana*, *Fraxinus excelsior*, *Populus tremula*,

Pinus sylvestris, Sorbus aucuparia and species of *Betula, Quercus, Salix* and *Ulmus*. However, it is most unlikely that the wind-blown sands of the west coast were ever colonised by trees. A major decline of woodland began between 5200 and 4000 years ago, and by 2500 BP the islands were predominantly treeless, the woods having been replaced by blanket peat (Bennett *et al.* 1990, Fossitt 1996). The possible causes of the woodland decline include climate change, human activities such as clearance and burning, and browsing by stock. Although there is insufficient evidence to establish the precise causes, Bennett *et al.* (1997) conclude that "it is difficult to escape the conclusion that the impact of early agriculturists and their grazing animals on fragile ecosystems were the most significant".

There is some direct evidence for the former presence of trees on our islands. The *Statistical Account* of 1792 reported that "frequently large pieces of trees are found in mosses; though now there is not a tree in it". These mosses were presumably on Coll, and further research in the interior of Coll might substantiate the view of the author of the account, Rev. Archibald M'Coll, that here "wood formerly grew in this parish, when thinly inhabited and fewer cattle reared" (Withrington & Grant 1983).

Aquatic habitats and swamps

One of the similarities between the Outer Hebrides and the islands of Coll and Tiree is the rich aquatic flora. This reflects the presence of lochs over a range of substrates from calcareous sand to acidic rocks and peat, which is reflected in corresponding range of vascular plant (and charophyte) species. It also suggests that geographical isolation is no barrier to the dispersal of aquatic plant species.

The survey of water bodies on the islands, as elsewhere in Britain, has concentrated on the identification of lake types rather than the description of the plant communities within the lakes (Preston *et al.* in press). Many lochs and pools on the exposed, acidic moorland of eastern Coll lack a well-developed emergent fringe and have a thin band of *Eleocharis multicaulis* round the edge and a species-poor aquatic flora dominated by isoetids such as *Isoetes echinospora, Littorella uniflora* and *Lobelia dortmanna* (A22). Other lochs in eastern Coll have larger stands of emergents around the edge, including *Carex rostrata* (S9), *Phragmites australis* (S4) and more notably *Carex lasiocarpa, Cladium mariscus* (S2) and *Schoenoplectus lacustris* (S8). *Eriocaulon aquaticum* grows in shallows at the edge of the larger lochs and in smaller pools (A22). In deeper water *Nymphaea alba* is often abundant (A7). The lochs on Tiree over stones and peat are subtly different. *Nymphaea alba* does not occur on the island, and many of the large emergents are also missing. However, some species are more frequent on Tiree than in similar lochs on Coll, including *Apium inundatum, Baldellia ranunculoides, Myriophyllum alterniflorum* and *Potentilla palustris*.

Table 2

National Vegetation Classification communities cited in the text

A7	*Nymphaea alba* community
A11	*Potamogeton pectinatus-Myriophyllum spicatum* community
A13	*Potamogeton perfoliatus-Myriophyllum alterniflorum* community
A22	*Litorella uniflora-Lobelia dortmanna* community
H10	*Calluna vulgaris-Erica cinerea* heath
M15	*Scirpus cespitosus-Erica tetralix* wet heath
M17	*Scirpus cespitosus-Eriophorum vaginatum* blanket mire
M23	*Juncus effusus/acutiflorus-Galium palustre* rush-pasture
M25	*Molinia caerulea-Potentilla erecta* mire
M29	*Hypericum elodes-Potamogeton polygonifolius* soakway
MC2	*Armeria maritima-Ligusticum scoticum* maritime rock crevice community
MC8	*Festuca rubra-Armeria maritima* maritime grassland
MC10	*Festuca rubra-Plantago* spp. maritime grassland
MG6	*Lolium perenne-Cynosurus cristatus* grassland
MG7	*Lolium perenne* leys and related grasslands
MG10	*Holcus lanatus-Juncus effusus* rush-pasture
MG11	*Festuca rubra-Agrostis stolonifera-Potentilla anserina* grassland
S2	*Cladium mariscus* swamp and sedge-beds
S4	*Phragmites australis* swamp and reed-beds
S8	*Scirpus lacustris* subsp. *lacustris* swamp
S9	*Carex rostrata* swamp
S19	*Eleocharis palustris* swamp
S20	*Scirpus lacustris* subsp. *tabernaemontani* swamp
S21	*Scirpus maritimus* swamp
SD2	*Cakile maritima-Honkenya peploides* strandline
SD3	*Martricaria maritima-Galium aparine* strandline
SD6	*Ammophila arenaria* mobile dune
SD7	*Ammophila arenaria-Festuca rubra* semi-fixed dune
SD8	*Festuca rubra-Galium verum* fixed dune community
SD17	*Potentilla anserina-Carex nigra* dune slack
SM13	*Puccinellia maritima* saltmarsh
SM16	*Festuca rubra* saltmarsh
U4	*Festuca ovina-Agrostis capillaris-Galium saxatile* grassland
U5	*Nardus stricta-Galium saxatile* grassland

Swamps and flushes leading down to acidic lochs may be dominated by *Eleogiton fluitans* or *Potamogeton polygonifolius*; occasionally *Hypericum elodes* is abundant in these communities, especially where a runnel broadens out into a shallow pool (M29).

Lochs and pools which are strongly influenced by the calcareous coastal sands lack many of the calcifuge species which are common elsewhere on the islands. They are often fringed by a dense low stand of *Eleocharis palustris* (S19). The northern pondweed *Potamogeton filiformis* (often accompanied by *Chara aspera*) grows in shallow water, especially over the sandier substrates (A13), and some of the species of deeper water (A11) include *Myriophyllum spicatum*, the broad-leaved pondweeds *Potamogeton perfoliatus* and its hybrid *P.* × *nitens*, the narrow-leaved species *P. pectinatus* and *P. pusillus* and a range of charophytes. In coastal sites the emergent fringe may be dominated by *Bolboschoenus maritimus* (S21) and *Schoenoplectus tabernaemontani* (S20).

Tiny rock pools on the tops of exposed, low cliffs on both Coll and Tiree provide an unusual habitat for a few salt-tolerant species. They may be dominated by *Myriophyllum spicatum*, *Potamogeton pectinatus*, *Ruppia maritima* or *Chara aspera*. The presence of aquatic vascular plants in such pools has received little attention. It is presumably only possible in climates where the input of water from rain or wind-driven sea spray balances losses from evaporation.

Burns and ditches in the acidic moorlands of Coll and Tiree have a rather mundane flora, usually consisting of some of the commoner calcifuge or tolerant aquatics such as *Carex nigra*, *Eleogiton fluitans*, *Hydrocotyle vulgaris*, *Potamogeton natans*, *P. polygonifolius* and *Ranunculus flammula*. The charophyte *Chara virgata* is also frequent in this habitat. Coastal streams and ditches in contact with calcareous sand are more interesting. The burns are often lined by *Iris pseudacorus* and *Sparganium erectum*; characteristic species on mud or in shallow water include *Callitriche stagnalis*, *Catabrosa aquatica*, *Lemna minor*, *Ranunculus trichophyllus*, *Rorippa nasturtium-aquaticum*, *Samolus valerandi*, *Veronica anagallis-aquatica* and *V. beccabunga*. The slow stream An Fhaodhail which flows through The Reef on Tiree is bordered by marshes and temporary ponds which together form a fascinating habitat. The stream is dominated over much of its length by the uncommon hybrid *Potamogeton* × *suecicus*; other notable species in this area include *Apium inundatum*, *A. nodiflorum*, *Berula erecta*, *Hippurus vulgaris*, *Myriophyllum alterniflorum*, *M. spicatum*, *Myosotis secunda*, *Oenanthe lachenalii*, *Potamogeton filiformis*, *P. pectinatus*, *P. pusillus*, *Schoenoplectus tabernaemontani* and *Utricularia vulgaris*. One other burn on Tiree is dominated by *Potamogeton* × *suecicus*, the outflow of Loch a'Phuill; this also has a flora which includes species tolerant of slightly brackish water such as *Myriophyllum spicatum*, *Potamogeton filiformis*, *P. pusillus* and *Ranunculus baudotii*.

Arable and pastures

There has been a massive decline in the amount of land under arable cultivation in both Tiree and Coll (see Table 3).

Ploughed land is now restricted to the occasional cultivated field and small vegetable patch on sandy soils. When we visited the islands in August 1997, we found two small fields and an open vegetable patch on Tiree and one potato field on Coll, although we did not carry out an exhaustive survey and these figures exclude cultivated land in gardens. The arable fields have a characteristic weed flora, including *Anagallis arvensis, Artemisia vulgaris, Atriplex patula, Chenopodium album, Chrysanthemum segetum, Fallopia convolvulus, Fumaria bastardii, Galeopsis bifida, Lamium confertum, Lamium hybridum, Papaver dubium, Persicaria maculosa, Rhinanthus minor, Sinapis arvensis* and *Urtica urens.*

Many arable weeds have declined since Heslop Harrison's day but their seeds are long lasting, and where a crop is grown plenty of weeds still appear.

A great deal of grassland has been improved at one time or another, with swards dominated by *Lolium perenne*, either with *Phleum pratense* (MG7) or with *Cynosurus cristatus* (MG6), being the most frequent. In the MG7 associations *Trifolium repens* and *Poa trivialis* are frequent. Wetter pastures that have 'gone back' have *Holcus lanatus* and *Juncus effusus* with much *Iris pseudacorus* (MG10). Grasslands that are frequently inundated by fresh or salt water have *Festuca rubra*, with *Agrostis stolonifera* and *Potentilla anserina* (MG11).

Table 3

The area of arable land (cereals, brassicas and potatoes) on Tiree and Coll, 1940–1981. Based on Harrison (1989, tables 3.1 and 3.2).

Year	Total area of arable land (hectares)		
	Tiree	Coll	Total
1940	596	113	709
1960	362	71	433
1981	172	61	233

LAND USE

Agriculture

The vegetation of both islands, but particularly Tiree, has been extensively modified by agricultural pressures. Tiree covers c. 7700 hectares and Coll c. 7400 hectares, so the very large numbers of people on the islands in the early 19th century must have had a particularly severe impact (Table 4). The population increase on Tiree from 1755 to 1831 is extraordinary, and may be a direct effect of the introduction of the smallpox vaccine, which was available after 1763, for before that date smallpox was a major cause of death. At this period most people were concentrated into the western half of Tiree. These high population levels proved to be unsustainable, and the collapse of the kelp industry coupled with the availability of lands for emigration quickly reduced numbers. Subsequently there has been a slow but remorseless decline in the population of both islands.

Coll has a completely different agricultural history to Tiree. In 1852 almost the entire population was cleared, and farmers from Ayrshire and Kintyre were encouraged to settle. For many years, until after the Second World War, Coll was famous for its cheese. Nowadays beef cattle are the norm, with sheep, but apart from Sorisdale in the north-east there is no crofting community.

The other major difference between the two islands is rabbits. Tiree has none, and they would pose an enormous threat to the stability of the extensive machair if they were ever introduced. Coll has plenty and there is currently an eradication programme to limit the damage they are causing to the sandy areas.

Macdonald (1811), MacCulloch (1824) and many later writers describe the effect of exposure on the agriculture of the islands. The soils are mainly sandy and light, being a mixture of shelly sand and peaty earths. Constant rainfall keeps them from drying out, but with no shelter it was, and is, essential not to disturb the turf for fear that the wind would blow the soil away. Indeed morphological evidence indicates severe wind erosion was widespread in the past, even as recently as the mid 19th century when population pressures were much higher (Mather *et al.* 1975). That same wind perpetually blows more calcareous sand over the pastures, renewing their fertility. During the 20th century the fall in population has been accompanied by a near cessation in arable cultivation and by a steady increase in cattle numbers on Tiree and sheep numbers on Coll. Harrison (1989) suggests that the latter is due to subsidies and support mechanisms, better production of hay and silage, and improved transport links. The effects of these changes have been shown both in the declines of arable weeds, and the conversion, through grazing, of heather moorland to grassland.

Table 4

Population of Tiree and Coll, 1755–1981. Based on figures provided by the national census returns for 1801–1901; earlier and later figures are cited from Darling (1955) and Boyd & Boyd (1990). There is a useful summary of the census returns for 1801–1851 in the report of the 1851 census. Figures prefixed by '?' are estimates as no census return was received.

Year	W Tiree	E Tiree	Tiree (total)	Coll
1755			1509	1193
1801			? 4001	1162
1811	? 2804	1138	3942	1277
1821	2964	1217	4181	1264
1831	3110	1343	4453	1316
1841	3242	1149*	4391	1442
1851	2591	1118	3709	1109
1861			3217	781
1871			2837	723
1881			2733	643
1891			2452	522
1901			2195	432
1951			1200	209
1981			800	140

* This is the first indication of a decline in population, and at that time was sufficiently remarkable to merit an explanatory note in the 1841 census report: "The decrease of population in the eastern district of Tyree island is attributed partly to emigration, and to 120 persons being absent in search of employment."

The type of grazing may well be a factor affecting plant distribution. Tiree has always had more cows than the mainland. Indeed Murray (1973) quotes a sheep to cattle ratio of 3:1 for Tiree compared with 16:1 for Mull. In the case of Tiree this means more hay meadows, more dung and a more tussocky habitat in wet ground caused by trampling.

Both islands, particularly Tiree, are affected by actions by conservation agencies to protect birds, particularly corncrakes (*Crex crex*). This should arrest the trend towards silage-making by encouraging late hay-cuts, but heavy stocking rates seem to be a permanent feature. Harrison (1989) points out that Tiree in particular is more fertile than all the other islands in the Hebrides, and that agriculture there is still based almost entirely on the crofting system.

Tiree has virtually no peat – indeed this was imported from Mull in the 19th century – but on Coll peat cutting has been practised in the past.

This is only a brief summary of those aspects of agricultural land use that are of most relevance to the botanist. There are good articles in Stroud (1989), which cover habitats and land use from an ornithological standpoint.

Conservation

In the last 15 years substantial parts of the islands have been designated Sites of Special Scientific Interest. Some of these sites have also received, or are about to receive, international status as Special Protection Areas and/or Special Areas of Conservation under the European Birds and Habitats directives respectively. Currently nature conservation designations of one form or another cover 25% of Tiree, all of Gunna and 52% of Coll. In addition to this all farmers and crofters on the islands are eligible to enter into an agri-environment scheme operated by the Scottish Executive Rural Affairs Department (SERAD). This scheme provides incentives for positive management for a wide variety of habitats and species including machair, herb-rich grassland, wetlands and early bird cover.

The RSPB own a nature reserve on Coll and lease a reserve on Tiree. With the co-operation of local grazing tenants they manage the reserves principally for corncrake, geese and wader populations.

NATIONALLY RARE AND SCARCE SPECIES

Three of the vascular plant species which are native to our area, *Eriocaulon aquaticum*, *Euphrasia heslop-harrisonii* and *Potamogeton rutilus*, are classified as rare in Britain as a whole because they are restricted to 15 or fewer 10km squares (Wigginton 1999). A further 18 species are scarce, i.e. they are found in 16–100 10km squares (Stewart *et al.* 1994). One species is listed as extinct in the wild by Wigginton (1999), *Agrostemma githago*, although this arable weed is an alien in Britain.

Most rare or scarce species on our islands are aquatics or coastal species. The aquatics are *Elatine hexandra*, *Eriocaulon aquaticum*, *Isoetes echinospora*, *Najas flexilis*, *Pilularia globulifera*, *Potamogeton coloratus*, *P. filiformis* and *P. rutilus*. Four charophytes, *Chara aspera*, *C. contraria*, *Nitella confervacea* and *Tolypella glomerata*, are also nationally scarce (Stewart 1996). The presence of so many uncommon aquatics reflects the range of habitats on the islands, as some are characteristic of base-rich waters (e.g. *Chara aspera*, *Potamogeton coloratus*) and others of base-poor sites (e.g. *Eriocaulon aquaticum*, *Isoetes echinospora*). There are also four nationally scarce species of wetland habitats, *Dactylorhiza traunsteineri*,

Deschampsia setacea, Hammarbya paludosa and *Spiranthes romanzoffiana;* this is also an ecologically heterogeneous group.

The rare and scarce species with distributions which are coastal, or at least predominantly coastal, include plants of sand or shingle beaches (*Atriplex praecox, Mertensia maritima*), saltmarshes (*Euphrasia heslop-harrisonii*), damp sandy soils (*Juncus balticus*) and coastal grassland (*Euphrasia foulaensis, Ophioglossum azoricum*). The remaining scarce species are *Ajuga pyramidalis* and *Pyrola media*, heathland plants, and the weedy *Polygonum boreale*.

One of the most striking features of the above rare and scarce species is the number that have been discovered on the islands in recent years. Only 10 of the 21 were known to Heslop Harrison *et al.* (1941). Of these, *Pyrola media* has not been seen subsequently, *Ajuga pyramidalis* appears to have declined, *Hammarbya paludosa* may have declined or may be overlooked and *Potamogeton coloratus* may have declined on Coll, although not on Tiree. *Mertensia maritima* has an unstable distribution, here as elsewhere, but there is no evidence for any decline, and the distribution of *Deschampsia setacea, Eriocaulon aquaticum, Juncus balticus, Potamogeton filiformis* and *Spiranthes romanzoffiana* appears to be stable, at least.

The possible decline of four scarce species since 1941 has been more than offset by the discovery of 11 on the islands since then. These were found in the 1940s (*Pilularia globulifera*), 1950s (*Isoetes echinospora*), 1960s (*Potamogeton rutilus*), 1980s (*Dactylorhiza traunsteineri, Elatine hexandra, Euphrasia heslop-harrisonii, Najas flexilis, Polygonum boreale*) and 1990s (*Atriplex praecox, Euphrasia foulaensis, Ophioglossum azoricum*). This list includes some plants which were taxonomically well-known in the 1930s but are inconspicuous, and others which have only been recognised in Britain since then. The only one which appears to be threatened on the islands is *Dactylorhiza traunsteineri*.

Of the 18 scarce species, 17 (94%) have been recorded since 1970. Typically, some 70–90% of scarce species have been recorded since 1970 from the vice-counties in NW Scotland (Stewart *et al.* 1994, Table 3), so the figure for our islands is not dissimilar to that expected in the area as a whole.

PHYTOGEOGRAPHY

Floristic elements on Tiree and Coll

Species may be classified into floristic elements based on their latitudinal and longitudinal distribution in the northern hemisphere (Preston & Hill 1997; Preston *et al.* 1997). The number of native species recorded from Tiree and Coll in these elements is given in Table 5; in Table 6 these figures are shown as a percentage of the total number of species recorded in these elements in Scotland. One endemic species (*Euphrasia heslop-harrisonii*) and three species of

Table 5

The number of species native to Tiree, Gunna and Coll in each floristic element. The eastern limit categories are as follows: 1 Ocea, Oceanic; 2 Subo, Suboceanic; 3 Euro, European; 4 Eurosib, Eurosiberian; 5 Euras, Eurasian; 6 Circ, Circumpolar. For the Mediterranean elements, 91 denotes Mediterranean-Atlantic; 92, Submediterranean-Subatlantic; 93, Mediterranean-montane.

	Eastern limit category						
Major biome category 1	2	3	4	5	6	
	Ocea	Subo	Euro	Eurosib	Euras	Circ	Total
1 Arctic-montane	-	-	-	-	-	1	1
2 Boreo-arctic Montane	-	-	4	-	-	6	10
3 Wide-boreal	-	-	-	1	1	13	15
4 Boreal-montane	5	1	10	3	-	17	36
5 Boreo-temperate	5	6	24	36	21	37	129
6 Wide-temperate	-	-	2	11	5	11	29
7 Temperate	13	19	78	24	10	10	154
8 Southern-temperate	2	13	37	27	6	6	91
9 Mediterranean	5	1	-	-	-	-	6
Total	**30**	**40**	**155**	**102**	**43**	**101**	**471**

uncertain world distribution (*Poa humilis, Utricularia ochroleuca, Zostera angustifolia*) are omitted from this table.

The 471 native species assigned to floristic elements from Tiree and Coll represent 44% of the native Scottish flora. The species in the Wide-boreal and Wide-temperate major biome categories (MBC), which have particularly broad world ranges, are particularly well represented on the islands. The only Scottish species in these elements which are absent from the islands are the Wide-boreal *Chrysosplenium alterniflorum* (which has an anomalous distribution) and *Cystopteris fragilis* and the Wide-temperate *Alisma plantago-aquatica, Ranunculus peltatus, Ruppia cirrhosa* and *Salicornia europaea*. There are three MBCs which make up the bulk of the Scottish flora, and of these the Boreo-temperate (62%) and Southern-temperate (50%) elements are better represented than the Temperate (41%). The relatively low proportion of Temperate species almost certainly reflects the virtual absence of native woodland on the islands, as many Temperate species are characteristic of woodland habitats whereas the Southern-temperate species are more often found in open habitats.

The most northerly and most southerly elements are poorly represented.

Table 6

The number of species native to Tiree, Gunna and Coll in each floristic element, expressed as a percentage of the total number in the element in Scotland. For explanation of the eastern limit categories and Mediterranean elements, see Table 5.

Major biome category	1 Ocea	2 Subo	Eastern limit category 3 Euro	4 Eurosib	5 Euras	6 Circ	Total
1 Arctic-montane	-	-	0	0	0	3	1
2 Boreo-arctic Montane	-	-	44	0	-	24	27
3 Wide-boreal	-	-	-	100	100	87	88
4 Boreal-montane	71	25	40	33	0	35	37
5 Boreo-temperate	83	86	62	61	58	61	62
6 Wide-temperate	.	.	67	100	100	79	88
7 Temperate	45	79	38	33	37	48	41
8 Southern-temperate	22	43	55	50	50	55	50
9 Mediterranean	21	7	0	-	-	-	15
Total	48*	60*	41*	47	49	43	44

* The Mediterranean elements are excluded from these percentages.

There is only a single Arctic-montane species (*Sedum rosea*) but ten Boreo-arctic Montane and 36 Boreal-montane species have been recorded. Five Mediterranean-Atlantic species (*Beta vulgaris, Calystegia soldanella, Catapodium marinum, Fumaria bastardii, Isolepis cernua*) and one Submediterranean-Subatlantic species (*Hypericum androsaemum*) are recorded, representing only 15% of the Scottish species and 5% of the British species in these elements.

The more northerly oceanic elements (Oceanic Boreal-montane and Boreo-temperate) are very well represented, a contrast to the under-represented Oceanic Southern-Temperate element. Four of the 17 hyperoceanic species recognised by Preston & Hill (1999) occur, two ferns (*Dryopteris aemula, Hymenophyllum wilsonii*) and two flowering plants (*Eriocaulon aquaticum, Spiranthes romanzoffiana*).

Relationship to the flora of Mull and the Outer Hebrides

The 475 species defined above as native to Tiree and Coll comprise 430 species which also occur as natives of Mull and a further 45 which are not recorded from the larger island. Almost all the 430 species common to both areas also occur in the Outer Hebrides. Fewer than 20 are absent from the Outer Hebrides, the most notable being *Carex hirta, Galeopsis speciosa, Geranium sanguineum, Hypericum androsaemum* and *H. tetrapterum. Allium vineale, Pyrola media* and *P. minor* were recorded from Coll by Heslop Harrison but have not been seen since, and are not known from the Outer Hebrides, whereas *Cerastium semidecandrum, Parnassia palustris* and *Pseudorchis albida* are known from the Outer Hebrides only as doubtful records. *Prunus spinosa* is apparently native to Coll but alien in the Outer Isles and we know of no record of the segregate *Festuca filiformis* from there.

The 45 species which are recorded from our islands but not on Mull are particularly interesting. The largest group are aquatic or wetland plants of calcareous, eutrophic or coastal waters. These include *Apium nodiflorum, Baldellia ranunculoides, Berula erecta, Carex diandra, C. elata, Dactylorhiza traunsteineri, Hippuris vulgaris, Juncus balticus, Potamogeton coloratus, P. filiformis, P. pusillus, P. rutilus, Ranunculus aquatilis, R. baudotii, R. lingua, R. trichophyllus, Typha latifolia* and *Veronica catenata.* Some of these species are found in both Tiree and Coll, perhaps the most widespread being *Baldellia ranunculoides, Hippuris vulgaris* and *Ranunculus aquatilis.* The rest are confined to Tiree, an indication of the greater prevalence of more base-rich wetlands there (Preston *et al.* in press). There are three plants of more acidic wetlands in our area which are absent from Mull, including the inconspicuous species *Deschampsia setacea* and *Pilularia globulifera* which might yet be discovered there and *Eriocaulon aquaticum,* which is unaccountably rare in Britain (Preston & Croft 1997).

There are several smaller groups of species which are absent from Mull, including terrestrial calcicoles (*Anacamptis pyramidalis, Astragalus danicus, Ononis repens*) and coastal species (*Atriplex laciniata, A. prostrata, Calystegia soldanella, Leymus arenarius*). These are also species which are found on Tiree and Coll or Tiree alone. The same is true of five species of disturbed or arable land (*Agrostis gigantea, Anthemis cotula, Bromus commutatus, Lamium hybridum* and *Potentilla reptans*), although we may be mistaken in regarding these as natives of our area. Other absentees from Mull are plants of dry heath (*Ajuga pyramidalis, Viola canina*), damp grassland (*Carex disticha, Spiranthes romanzoffiana*) and moist turf near the sea (*Trifolium fragiferum*).

The remaining species which are not reported from Mull are recent segregates or taxonomically critical plants which in some cases have only been found in our area in recent years and may still be discovered on the larger island. They are *Atriplex praecox, Euphrasia foulaensis, E. heslop-harrisonii, Galeopsis bifida, Juncus ambiguus, Ophioglossum azoricum* and *Polygonum boreale.*

No fewer than 37 of the 45 species which are absent from Mull are recorded in the Outer Hebrides by Pankhurst & Mullin (1991). The only exceptions are seven species which have not been recorded from the Outer Isles (*Astragalus danicus, Bromus commutatus, Carex elata, Dactylorhiza traunsteineri, Eriocaulon aquaticum, Ranunculus lingua, Typha latifolia*) and one where the record requires confirmation (*Potentilla reptans*). These figures demonstrate the ecological similarities between our islands and the Outer Hebrides, which were first pointed out by Macvicar (1897a) and later emphasised by Heslop Harrison (1941a).

It is not surprising that many species which occur in v.c. 103 on the large and varied island of Mull are absent from the smaller islands of Tiree and Coll with their much less variable geology and topography. Over 160 of the species recorded as natives of Mull by Jermy & Crabbe (1978) are not known from Tiree and Coll. In some cases the reasons are clearly climatic. Twenty of the absent species are classified by Preston & Hill (1997) as Arctic-montane, for example. These range from the relatively widespread *Alchemilla alpina* and *Saxifraga aizoides* to the rare *Koenigia islandica*. However, many are relatively common species of Boreo-temperate or Temperate distributions which are almost certainly absent because of the lack of woodland or ungrazed tall-herb communities. These include the Boreo-temperate *Geum rivale* and *Glechoma hederacea* and the Temperate species *Circaea lutetiana, Eupatorium cannabinum, Moehringia trinervia* and *Sanicula europaea*. There are also species of Southern-temperate affinity which are absent as natives, such the Suboceanic *Digitalis purpurea* and the more widespread *Convolvulus arvensis* and *Euphorbia peplus,* although it is often difficult to say whether or not the species in these elements are native in a particular vice-county. Some 70 of these 160 species are known from the Outer Hebrides, including some of the more widespread Arctic-montane species.

Over 40 species are found in the Outer Hebrides but not on Mull, Tiree or Coll (the exact number depends on how one reconciles differences in allocating plants to native and alien categories in different floras). These include a few Arctic-montane and Boreo-arctic Montane species which occur at sea-level on the dune systems of the Outer Hebrides (*Carex maritima, Equisetum variegatum*) and, more surprisingly, Arctic-montane species which are normally found at high altitudes in Britain (*Epilobium anagallidifolium, Euphrasia frigida, Juncus trifidus*). Several species are aquatic plants which are found in eutrophic or brackish water (*Callitriche hermaphroditica, Potamogeton crispus, P. friesii, Ruppia cirrhosa, Zannichellia palustris*), three are endemic *Euphrasia* species (*E. campbelliae, E. marshallii, E. rotundifolia*) and two are coastal plants with Mediterranean- or Submediterranean-Atlantic distributions (*Catapodium rigidum, Crithmum maritimum*). The remaining species are a heterogeneous group. Many have are restricted to a single locality in the Outer Hebrides (*Cicuta virosa, Cruciata laevipes, Dactylorhiza lapponica, Juncus filiformis, Lycopodiella inundata, Oenanthe fistulosa, Rorippa islandica*) or are known only from old records (*Equisetum pratense, Valerianella dentata*) or both (*Carex acutiformis, Eriophorum latifolium, Ranunculus sardous*). However, some are more widespread, including *Aphanes arvensis sens. str., Cochlearia anglica, Crambe*

Table 7

Native species present on Tiree but not Coll, or *vice versa*.

Species in brackets were last recorded before 1987. 'G' indicates that the species is recorded from Gunna. Microspecies, infraspecific taxa and hybrids are excluded. Segregates which are almost certainly under-recorded are marked with an asterisk.

Major biome category	Species confined to Coll	Species confined to Tiree
Boreo-arctic Montane	Empetrum nigrum (G)	Juncus balticus
	Eriophorum vaginatum (G)	Leymus arenarius
		Mertensia maritima (G)
Wide-boreal	Hieracium murorum agg.	
Boreal-montane	(Ajuga pyramidalis)	Euphrasia foulaensis
	(Alchemilla filicaulis)	Polygonum boreale
	Arctostaphylos uva-ursi	
	Atriplex praecox	
	Carex lasiocarpa	
	Carex limosa	
	Drosera anglica	
	Eriocaulon aquaticum	
	Euphrasia scottica	
	Isoetes lacustris	
	(Listera cordata)	
	Najas flexilis	
	Potamogeton alpinus	
	(Pseudorchis albida)	
	(Pyrola media)	
	(Pyrola minor)	
	Saxifraga hypnoides	
	Spiranthes romanzoffiana	
	(Subularia aquatica)	
Boreo-temperate	Betula pubescens	Carex diandra
	Equisetum sylvaticum	(Dactylorhiza traunsteineri)
	(Euphrasia confusa)	Galeopsis speciosa
	Hymenophyllum wilsonii	Ophioglossum azoricum
	Juniperus communis	Silene dioica

	Melampyrum pratense	
	Oxalis acetosella	
	(Phegopteris connectilis)	
	Populus tremula	
	Rhynchospora alba	
	Rosa mollis	
	Salix cinerea	
	Sorbus aucuparia	
Wide-temperate	Schoenoplectus lacustris	
Temperate	*Agrostis vinealis	(Aphanes arvensis sens. lat.)
	(Allium vineale)	Astragalus danicus
	Asplenium ruta-muraria	Carex caryophyllea
	Cerastium semidecandrum	(Carex elata)
	(Chrysosplenium oppositi-	Elatine hexandra
	folium)	Ononis repens
	Corylus avellana	Pilularia globulifera
	Dryopteris aemula	Platanthera chlorantha
	Luzula sylvatica	Ranunculus lingua
	Lycopus europaeus (G)	
	Lysimachia nemorum	
	Nymphaea alba	
	Oreopteris limbosperma	
	(Polystichum aculeatum)	
	(Potentilla sterilis)	
	Prunus spinosa	
	Rosa canina	
	(Veronica catenata)	
Southern-temperate	Cladium mariscus	Agrostis gigantea
	*Erodium lebelii	(Anthemis cotula)
	Hedera helix	Apium nodiflorum
	Juncus maritimus	*Erodium cicutarium sens.
str.		
	Osmunda regalis	Festuca arundinacea
	Trifolium fragiferum	Potamogeton pusillus
		(Typha latifolia)
Mediterranean	Hypericum androsaemum	
	(Isolepis cernua)	
Endemic	Euphrasia heslop-harrisonii	
Unknown	Rorippa microphylla (G)	
	*Utricularia ochroleuca	

maritima, Dactylorhiza majalis, Epilobium hirsutum, Erophila glabrescens, Gentianella amarella, Hierochloe odorata, Potamogeton epihydrus, Puccinellia distans, Rorippa sylvestris, Salix myrsinifolia, S. phylicifolia, Spergularia rupicola and *Stellaria neglecta.*

Differences between Coll and Tiree

The phytogeographical analysis throws some light on the difference between the floras of Tiree and Coll (Table 7). Most of the 64 species present on Coll but not Tiree belong to the Boreal-montane, Boreo-temperate and Temperate elements whereas there is a somewhat less marked tendency for the 26 species present on Tiree but not Coll to be concentrated in the Temperate and Southern-temperate elements.

Distribution of wetland and aquatic plant species

The survey of aquatic habitats by CDP and NFS in 1989 and 1990 provides a detailed picture of the recent distribution of aquatic plant species on the islands (Figs 4–9). The restriction of some species of acidic habitats to eastern Coll (Fig. 4) is striking. Although this is the area where acidic lochs are most frequent, it is not clear whether these distributions simply reflect the ecological requirements of the species or whether these plants are unable to colonise suitable habitats elsewhere (e.g. in central Tiree) because of poor dispersal abilities. The restricted distribution of *Eriocaulon aquaticum* in Britain has often been discussed, and it is interesting to see from these detailed maps how its distribution on Coll is not anomalous, but matches that of several other species. Species which are found on both islands but are more frequent on Coll also tend to be those of acidic habitats (Fig. 5), whereas those confined to Tiree, or more widespread there than on Coll, are plants of eutrophic or more or less base-rich habitats (Fig. 6). The other maps are of widespread or coastal species (Figs 7–9). In interpreting these maps it is important to realise that they are primarily based on lake surveys, and probably underestimate the distribution of species which extend into moist terrestrial habitats.

Figure 4

Distribution of some aquatic plant species confined to Coll. The map is based on recent records (1987 onwards) which are localised to 1km squares.

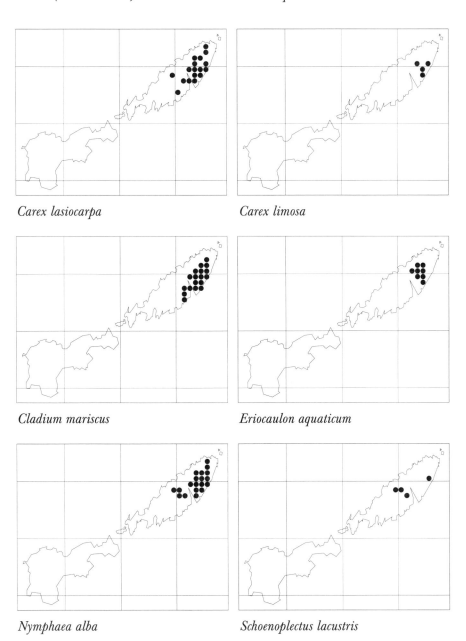

Carex lasiocarpa

Carex limosa

Cladium mariscus

Eriocaulon aquaticum

Nymphaea alba

Schoenoplectus lacustris

35

Figure 5 *Distribution of some wetland or aquatic plant species which are more frequent on Coll than Tiree. The map is based on those recent records (1987 onwards) which are localised to 1km squares. As most records are derived from lake surveys, the maps may underestimate the distribution of wetland species which also occur in other habitats.*

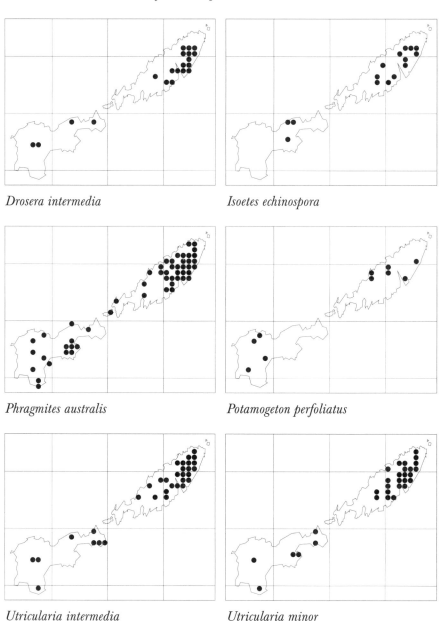

Drosera intermedia

Isoetes echinospora

Phragmites australis

Potamogeton perfoliatus

Utricularia intermedia

Utricularia minor

Figure 6

Distribution of some wetland or aquatic plant species which are confined to Tiree, or more widespread on Tiree than Coll. For source of records, see legend to Fig. 5.

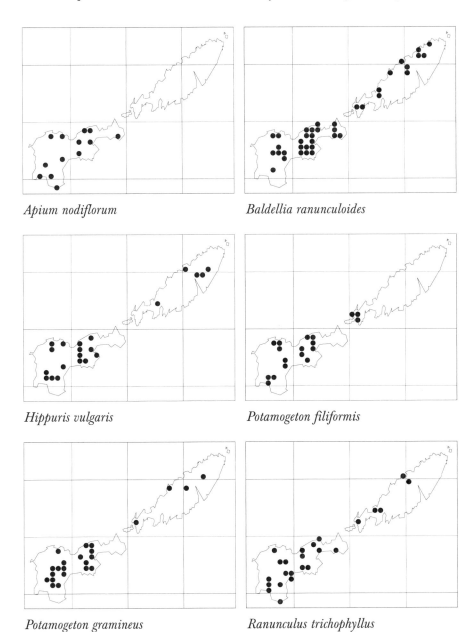

Apium nodiflorum

Baldellia ranunculoides

Hippuris vulgaris

Potamogeton filiformis

Potamogeton gramineus

Ranunculus trichophyllus

Figure 7

Distribution of some wetland or aquatic plant species which are widespread on Tiree and Coll (1). For source of records, see legend to Fig. 5. Records of Cyperaceae (Carex, Eleocharis, Eleogiton) from a 1km square survey of Tiree have also been included.

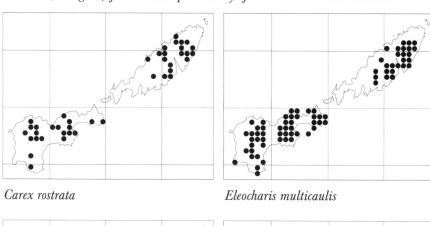

Carex rostrata   Eleocharis multicaulis

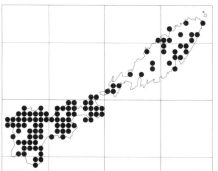
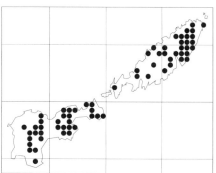

Eleocharis palustris   Eleogiton fluitans

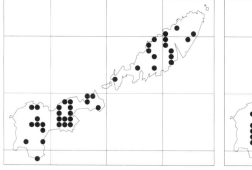
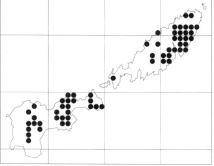

Equisetum fluviatile   Littorella uniflora

Figure 8

Distribution of some wetland or aquatic plant species which are widespread on Tiree and Coll (2). For source of records, see legend to Fig. 5.

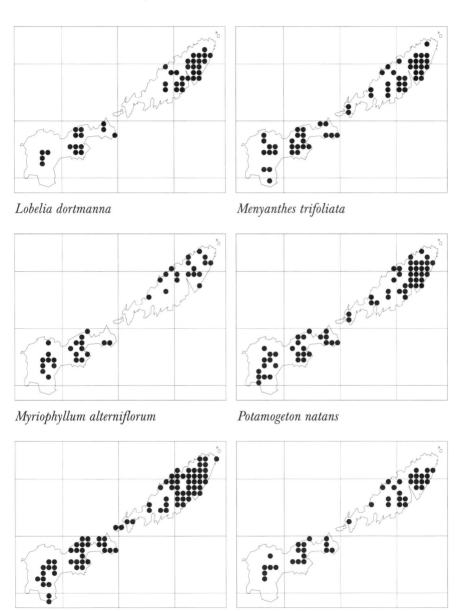

Lobelia dortmanna

Menyanthes trifoliata

Myriophyllum alterniflorum

Potamogeton natans

Potamogeton polygonifolius

Sparganium angustifolium

Figure 9

Distribution of some coastal wetland or aquatic plant species. For source of records, see legend to Fig. 5.

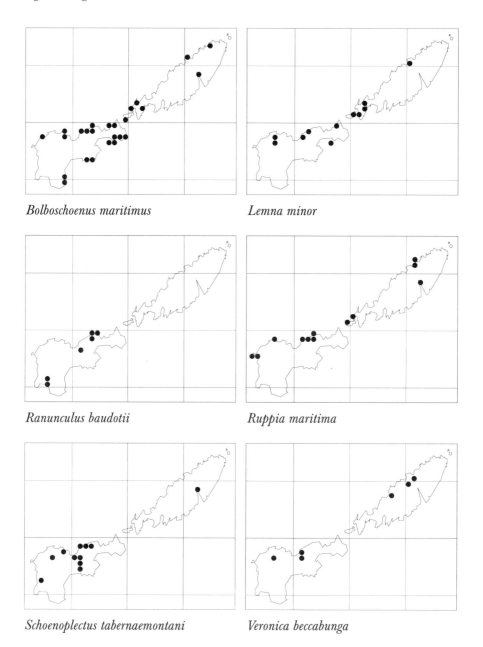

Bolboschoenus maritimus

Lemna minor

Ranunculus baudotii

Ruppia maritima

Schoenoplectus tabernaemontani

Veronica beccabunga

HISTORY OF BOTANICAL RECORDING

Early records

Tiree and Coll have been well recorded compared with most islands in the Inner and Outer Hebrides.

   The first botanical records from the islands are found in the descriptive tours of the Western Isles made in the 18th and early 19th centuries. Martin (1703) visited Coll but recorded no wild plants. The Rev. Dr John Walker visited both Coll and Tiree in 1764, but although he was a notable naturalist (Taylor 1959), there are only incidental mentions of plants in his Report on his Hebridean journeys. The 'Natural History of the Hebrides' which Walker planned was never completed, and the Report was published only recently (McKay 1980). On 'Tirey' he was most impressed by the Rieve [The Reef], "a plain...of the same dead level throughout...About the first of June when the cattle are put upon it, it is all over as white as a cloth, with Daises *[Bellis perennis]*, and White Clover *[Trifolium repens]*. In that Season, there may be seen pasturing upon it at once, about 1,000 Black Cattle, 2,000 Sheep and 300 Horses intermixed with immense Flocks of Lapwings and Green Plovers." On Coll Walker describes a bay on the north side, which "in the Month of July appeared very remarkable. It is a circular plain, about half a mile over, like so much bowling Green Ground, surrounded with Hills. It is a rich sandy Soil, which is entirely filled with red and yellow Clover, a variety of yellow Ranunculus's and a vast Profusion of the Bloody Cranesbill *[Geranium sanguineum]* and other Flowers, which altogether, form the most beautiful embroidered Carpet...". The island was "entirely destitute of Wood...bears neither Tree nor Shrub, except what are in Mr Macleans Garden; and the small grey willow [surely *Salix aurita*], which is cut down by the Cattle as fast as it rises." The only other wild plant he mentions is "the *Arundo Arenaria* of Linnaeus *[Ammophila arenaria]*, a coarse hard grass, that grows in great Quantity upon the Hills of blowing Sand". The young leaves were eaten by the cattle in spring and the mature leaves woven to make sacks ("with no small Toil, and a good deal of Art") and twisted to make ropes and cables.

   Samuel Johnson and James Boswell were driven to seek refuge on Coll by storms when they were travelling from Skye to Mull on their tour of the Hebrides in October 1773 (Boswell 1785, Johnson 1775, Lascelles 1971). Johnson provided a graphic description of the topography of the island: "Col is not properly rocky; it is rather one continued rock, of a surface much diversified with protuberances, and covered with a thin layer of earth, which is often broken, and discovers the stone. Such a soil is not for plants that strike deep roots; and perhaps on the whole island nothing has ever yet grown to the height of a table". Unfortunately the season was too late to expect botanical records, though Boswell was told that in summer the turf at Breachacha was "enamelled with clover and daisies".

John MacCulloch's (1819, 1824) descriptions of the islands of Coll and Tiree are primarily geological, but he did note a few of the more notable plant species. Like Dr Johnson he was struck by the treelessness of the islands but he described it in rather less homely language, stating of Tiree that "with the exception of the *Salix argentea* of Smith, (the *arenaria* of Lightfoot) [*S. repens*], it may truly be said not to possess a ligneous fibre". He also noted the abundance of white clover [*Trifolium repens*] in the pastures of Tiree and that "the regular state of moisture in the soil is everywhere indicated by the *Iris pseudacorus, Polygonum viviparum* [an obvious error, presumably for *Persicaria amphibia*], and other aquatic plants, which are found flourishing in every corn field; little concern being felt, in the Highland system of farming, about the growth of weeds". On Coll MacCulloch noted some of the commoner species of the western dunes, including *Carex arenaria, Elytrigia juncea, Galium verum* and on a small tract, "a profusion of the brilliant crimson flowers of *Geranium sanguineum*". He also recorded *Gymnadenia conopsea, Listera ovata, Lobelia dortmanna, Nymphaea alba, Orchis mascula, Osmunda regalis* "abundantly in the interior and moister parts of the island", *Potamogeton gramineus, Rosa pimpinellifolia, Sedum anglicum* and *Thalictrum minus.* His record of *Himantoglossum hircinum* (as *Satyrium hircinum*) is an obvious error, and *Crambe maritima* "in abundance along the sandy shores on the western side" may be an error for *Cakile maritima*, as Macvicar (1896) implied, though *Crambe maritima* does occur very rarely in the Western Isles. However, there is no doubt about MacCulloch's outstanding discovery, *Eriocaulon aquaticum* "growing in some of the central lakes in company with *Lobelia dortmanna*". This is still present in this area and is perhaps the most notable rarity on the island.

Other visitors may have botanised on Coll but left no written record, one example being the Rev. E. Bell (1829–1904) whose specimen of *Catabrosa aquatica* in **CGE** is the only evidence we know of the presence of a botanist on the island in July 1867. Bell was a clergyman who wrote a book *The Primrose and Darwinism* "to demonstrate that Darwin's theories on the cross-fertilisation of plants were radically unsound" (Horwood & Noel 1933). The first primarily botanical account of one of our islands is that resulting from Thomas Scott's visit in 1879. Scott took advantage of the offer of a free passage to make "a two day's ramble over the Island of Coll", later publishing notes on some of the plants he saw (Scott 1881). These included the first records of some of the more interesting species, including *Ajuga pyramidalis* "in a few places", *Catapodium marinum* "on the walls of the old castle of the MacLeans" and *Cladium mariscus* "in the small loch behind the overseer's new house". Like Walker, he was impressed by "*Geranium sanguineum*, in most beautiful profusion".

The work of Macvicar and Heslop Harrison

Symers Macvicar (1857–1932) trained as a doctor and settled in 1888 at Invermoidart, living there for the rest of his life. Today he is known for his works on British hepatics, but his earlier research, marked by painstaking accuracy, covered the botany of Westerness and Lismore, as well as Tiree and Coll. He visited both islands in 1896, and Tiree again in 1897. He commented on *Eriocaulon* (Macvicar 1896, 1897c), and on interesting plants (Macvicar 1897a, 1897b). But his lasting achievement was a substantial paper on the flora of Tiree (Macvicar 1898), which covered 320 taxa, excluding Characeae, and gave localities for the rarer species and frequency details for all taxa.

Surprisingly this scholarly work was not referred to by J. W. Heslop Harrison (1881–1967) who with fellow academics and students from King's College, Newcastle upon Tyne, a satellite of University of Durham, initiated a series of ecological and biogeographical studies of the Inner and Outer Hebrides from 1935. His son George visited the islands in 1935, and returned with his future brother-in-law, Dr W. A. Clark, in 1937. Then during 1939 and 1940, J. W. Heslop Harrison, his daughter Helena Heslop Harrison, Dr Clark and R. B. Cooke, with their students (John Heslop Harrison, G. E. M. Hardy, C. S. Pittendrigh and J. A. Richardson), spent three lengthy periods on Coll, Tiree and Gunna. Richardson (1970) was eventually to write Heslop Harrison's obituary in *Watsonia*. The result of these visits was *The Flora of the Isles of Coll, Tiree and Gunna (V.C. 110B)* (Heslop Harrison *et al.* 1941), in which 573 species, segregates and hybrids were recorded.

Heslop Harrison's doubtful records

Heslop Harrison's publications on the flora and fauna of the Outer Isles immediately attracted attention as they included a number of most unexpected discoveries. These gave rise to grave suspicion that they were introductions (Raven 1949) and many botanists concluded that Heslop Harrison had either practised or been the victim of deliberate fraud. This has cast a shadow over all his work in the Hebrides. Our experience is that in general the Flora of Coll and Tiree is still an excellent guide to the plants of the islands, and clearly reveals his thorough knowledge of the terrain and his eye for habitat. Some of the species reported have never been refound (Table 8). In only a few cases are there obvious reasons for the lack of further records: agricultural change explains the disappearance of *Agrostemma githago* from Coll (as from the rest of Britain), for example, and taxonomic revision the lack of any later records of *Ranunculus fluitans*. Most other species must either be rare plants on the islands which have eluded later visitors or errors in identification. Heslop Harrison and his team must inevitably have discovered rare taxa during their long sojourn on the islands. Some of these have only recently been rediscovered

Table 8

List of species, subspecies and hybrids recorded by Heslop Harrison *et al.* (1941) and never refound. Taxa marked with an asterisk have been reported subsequently but we regard the later records as dubious. Records of *Taraxacum* species are excluded as the broad species recognised by Heslop Harrison cannot be equated to modern species concepts.

Agrostemma githago
Alchemilla filicaulis subsp. *filicaulis*
Allium vineale
*Arctium minus subsp. *minus*
Callitriche hermaphroditica
Carex appropinquata
C. bigelowii
C. curta
C. elata
C. laevigata
C. riparia
C. sylvatica
Conringia orientalis
Dactylorhiza incarnata × *maculata*
D. incarnata × *purpurella*
D. majalis subsp. *occidentalis*
Dryopteris carthusiana
Euphrasia arctica × *confusa*
E. confusa
E. confusa × *micrantha*
E. curta
E. frigida
Fumaria muralis subsp. *boraei*
F. purpurea
*Galium uliginosum
Geranium pratense
G. pusillum
Hieracium subcrocatum
H. vulgatum (see note below)
Isolepis cernua
*Leontodon hispidus
Listera cordata
Mentha aquatica × *spicata*

M. spicata
Persicaria hydropiper × *maculosa*
Potentilla sterilis
Pyrola media
P. minor
Ranunculus fluitans
Rhinanthus angustifolius
Rosa pimpinellifolia × *sherardii*
Rubus conjugens
R. radula
Salix aurita × *cinerea* subsp. *oleifolia*
S. aurita × *viminalis*
*S. myrsinifolia
Scrophularia nodosa
Senecio sylvaticus
Sisyrinchium bermudiana
*Sparganium emersum
Spergularia rubra
Subularia aquatica
Torilis japonica
Trifolium bocconei
*Trisetum flavescens
Veronica montana
V. polita
Viola reichenbachiana
Vulpia bromoides
*Zannichellia palustris
Zostera noltii

Note: *Hieracium vulgatum* was collected by R. B. Cooke in 1939 but not reported by Heslop Harrison *et al.* (1941) in the published Flora.

(e.g. *Equisetum* × *trachyodon, Trifolium fragiferum*) and others presumably await rediscovery. Equally inevitably, the Newcastle team must have made errors of identification, as we all do. It is difficult to decide between these alternatives for individual taxa, especially if (as with *Fumaria purpurea* and *Rhinanthus angustifolius*) the species might have been affected by subsequent agricultural change. We have tended to accept records if they are consistent with the distribution of the plant elsewhere in western Scotland, and in particular in Mull (Jermy & Crabbe 1978), Skye and other islands in v.c. 104 (Murray 1980) and the Outer Hebrides (Pankhurst & Mullin 1991). We have rejected records if they appear to be at variance with the distribution in these areas, or are for plants with a history of taxonomic confusion. Reasons for our decisions are outlined in the species accounts. These decisions will need to be reviewed in the light of further fieldwork. It is likely that some species may actually be absent from the islands even though they occur in nearby areas and have been accepted in the current list. Other species in Table 8, quite probably including some which we have rejected as probable errors, may be confirmed as occurring.

There are only two outstandingly rare species listed in Table 8. One is *Trifolium bocconei*, a Mediterranean-Atlantic species which reaches its northern world limit on the Lizard peninsula in Cornwall. It clearly falls into the same group of phytogeographically unexpected species as *Carex lachenalii, C. norvegica* and *C. rariflora*, Arctic-montane species reported by Heslop Harrison from the Outer Hebrides, and *C. bicolor* and *Polycarpon tetraphyllum*, Arctic-montane and Mediterranean-Atlantic species which he reported from Rum. The supposed presence of plants (and invertebrates) of such diverse geographical affinities was used by Heslop Harrison (1939c, 1941a) to argue that the Hebridean flora had "survived the Glacial Period in a much more extensive 'Long Island' than exists today". Heslop Harrison *et al.* (1941) describe the circumstances under which *T. bocconei* was discovered on Coll in some detail:

> "A party of our students, who collected on Coll in September 1939, discovered *Trifolium fragiferum* near Caoles and brought a large number of specimens home. Amongst these were three examples of the present species. A map showing the positions worked was drawn, and four of us spent a long time on the ground in 1940. However, despite our careful searches, no further specimens turned up; we learn that this uncertainty in appearances characterises the species everywhere."

Although it is not totally impossible that *Trifolium bocconei* grew on Coll, it is very unlikely that it did so. Not only is this phytogeographically unlikely, but on ecological grounds one would not expect *T. bocconei* to grow with *T. fragiferum*, as *T. bocconei* is a plant of thin soil over rocky outcrops, and is intolerant of waterlogging in winter (D. E. Coombe, pers. comm.), whereas *T. fragiferum* is a plant of heavy or saline, often winter-flooded sites, which on Coll grows on a damp streamside. The circumstances of the discovery of *T. bocconei* would clearly have allowed someone to slip three specimens into the collection of *T. fragiferum*. We have rejected the record on the grounds that it is probably fraudulent.

The second rarity reported by Heslop Harrison *et al.* (1941) is *Sisyrinchium bermudiana* (*S. angustifolium*), described as "another member of the Irish-American element". This has never been refound, although the BSBI party carried out a special search for it in 1967. *S. bermudiana* has not otherwise been claimed as a native species for Scotland, though it is widespread as a possible native in western Ireland. A third species which was remarkable when reported as a possible native of Coll by Heslop Harrison *et al.* (1941) is *Epilobium ciliatum*, although this North American species has subsequently spread to the islands as an alien. It was because of the presence of *Eriocaulon aquaticum*, *Sisyrinchium bermudiana*, *Spiranthes romanzoffiana* and to a lesser extent *Epilobium ciliatum* on Coll that Heslop Harrison (1941a) concluded that "for its headquarters in the Hebrides, the American element possesses the Isle of Coll ... the concentration of the American element in Coll recalls a similar grouping in Ireland, thereby indicating the possibility of a land connexion between Coll and Ireland long after the Outer Hebrides had parted company from both". Although the presence of *Eriocaulon aquaticum* and *Spiranthes romanzoffiana* is well documented, we have not accepted the record of *Sisyrinchium bermudiana* in view of the failure of later botanists to find it. Similarly we do not accept the early record of *Epilobium ciliatum*, though the uncharacteristically tentative suggestion by Heslop Harrison that this may have been native suggests that this is not likely to have been a deliberate fraud.

In reviewing in detail Heslop Harrison's records from Tiree and Coll, we have reached similar conclusions to those of Sabbagh (1999) in his book *A Rum Affair*. Many of the discoveries were undoubtedly genuine, including those of *Equisetum* × *trachyodon*, *Spiranthes romanzoffiana* and *Trifolium fragiferum*. Some (which have not attracted much attention) are probably mundane misidentifications. At least one of the Coll records, *Trifolium bocconei*, is almost certainly fraudulent, made with the intention of strengthening the theories of the vegetational history of the islands espoused by Heslop Harrison. Although no conclusive proof that Heslop Harrison himself was responsible for these fraudulent records has come to light, the cumulative weight of evidence reviewed by Sabbagh (1999) leaves us in little doubt that he was responsible. Finally, there are doubtful cases (such as *Epilobium ciliatum* and *Sisyrinchium bermudiana*) which may be genuine discoveries which have eluded later botanists, misidentifications or fraudulent claims. These records can only be rejected as unconfirmed, pending further evidence.

Post-war fieldwork

Since 1945 many private visits have been made (Table 9), but noteworthy are two BSBI pairs of visits. In 1967 Miss U. K. Duncan led a group of about seven members to Coll, and the following year a group of about eight members to Tiree (Duncan 1968a,b, 1969, 1970). We know of five of the members of the Coll party, Miss Duncan, Dr Larch Garrad, now BSBI recorder for the Isle of Man, Miss F. M. Jarrett from Kew, P. D. Bacon and Joan Clark, but unfortunately none of the other participants. Dr Garrad writes that much time was spent searching for Heslop Harrison's plants. Miss Duncan was unable to take her car to Coll, as the pier was being rebuilt, and the party therefore had only one small hire car at their disposal. Larch Garrad's main memory, as one of the younger members of the party, is of the interminable walking from place to place. She was hampered too, she says, by too much drinking with the men building the pier! These meetings resulted in cards listing the species recorded in the main 10km squares, and in herbarium specimens of critical taxa collected by Miss Duncan and deposited in **BM**.

The 10km squares NL 93 (Tiree) and NM 26 (Coll) were selected for recording in the BSBI Monitoring Scheme in 1987–1988. The Tiree square was recorded by Lynne Farrell and Ro Scott. Joan Clark did most of the recording for the Monitoring Scheme on Coll, ably supported by Paddy Braithwaite, Brian Brookes, Barbara and Ken Cassels, Henry Noltie, Agnes Walker and Peter Wormell. Then in 1989 Agnes Walker, by then the vice-county recorder, organised a BSBI meeting which resulted in a visit by at least 14 members to Coll, and followed it up with a trip the next year to Tiree on which 27 members appeared for all or part of the week. The records made on these field meetings form the basis for our recent coverage of the islands, but we have not been able to locate all the field cards compiled on these visits.

Two other surveys have provided valuable records: the vegetation survey of Tiree by Dargie (1993) and the Scottish Natural Heritage Loch Survey, which visited the islands in 1994. Records from the latter come from specimens of *Potamogeton* examined by CDP and charophytes determined by N. F. Stewart.

Of the current authors, CDP, in conjunction with N. F. Stewart, sampled almost all the lochs in 1989 and 1990, whilst DAP recorded the Cyperaceae from 1km squares on Tiree in 1990. Simon Leach of NCC looked at the salt-marshes on both islands. DAP and CDP, joined for some of the time by Agnes Walker, revisited both islands in 1997 specifically to fill gaps in the records.

Table 9

Recording visits to the islands, 1941–1999

1947	Cards from I. A. Williams (10km square lists on cards at BRC based on specimens at **BM** determined by A. J. Wilmott. Some of Williams' specimens are incorporated at **BM** but we have been unable to find others).
1947	J. Heslop Harrison, visit to study *Dactylorhiza* (J. Heslop Harrison 1949).
1951	C. W. Muirhead (specimens at **BM**, **E** and **CLE**); W. A. Vincent (specimens from Tiree at **BM**).
1952	K. N. G. Macleay (Wallace 1954); H. G. Powell, J. B. Spence and P. B. Vose, study of machair vegetation (Vose et al. 1957).
1959	A. McG. Stirling (BRC).
1960	V. Gordon (BRC).
1961	A. Dale (specimens at **E**).
1967	BSBI/BSE meeting on Coll led by U. K. Duncan (1968a,b; BRC; specimens at **BM** and **K**).
1967	Dr L. Garrad (card index).
1968	BSBI/BSE meeting on Tiree led by U. K. Duncan (1969, 1970; BRC; specimens at **BM**).
1973	C. J. Cadbury; D. C. Lang.
1975	C. J. Cadbury.
1978	R. E. C. Ferreira (Farrell 1983).
1980	L. Farrell and J. MacIntosh (Farrell 1983).
1981	A. Currie.
1982	M. Barron, J. W. Clark, A. A. P. Slack and A. McG. Stirling.
1983	K. P. Bland; C. J. Cadbury; J. W. Clark; B. J. Coppins; P. Wormell.
1984	J. W. Clark, A. C. Jermy and A. Walker; S. Haywood; V. M. Morgan (rare species survey).
1985	J. W. Clark; A. Walker.
1986	J. W. Clark and A. Walker.
1987	Recording for BSBI Monitoring Scheme, by P. F. Braithwaite, B. K. & K. A. H. Cassels, J. W. Clark, H. J. Noltie, A. Walker and P. Wormell; C. J. Cadbury; L. Farrell.
1988	Recording for BSBI Monitoring Scheme, by K. P. Bland, P. F. Braithwaite, B. S. Brookes, B. K. & K. A. H. Cassels, J. W. Clark, L. Farrell, R. Scott and A. Walker; B. Rae.
1989	BSBI meeting on Coll led by A. Walker with E. Buckle, A. Daly, B. Gale, M. A. R. & C. Kitchen, S. J. Leach, J. Mackay, V. M. Morgan, C. D. Preston, H. E. Stace, N. F. Stewart, P. Taylor; J. W. Clark; F. Horsman.
1990	BSBI meeting on Tiree led by A. Walker with G. M. Barter, C. J. Bruxner, E. Buckle, P. Cashman, J. W. Clark, D. Counsell, J. G. Dury,

	J. Grimshaw, P. Harden, A. Hold, A. Horsfall, M. G. B. Hughes, M. A. R. & C. Kitchen, V. M. Morgan, C. W. Murray, D. A. & A. V. Pearman, C. D. Preston, E. Stewart, N. F. Stewart, A. McG. Stirling, P. Taylor, B. H. & B. S. Thompson, S. D. Webster.
1991	J. W. Clark; F. Horsman.
1992	J. W. Clark; P. E. Bellamy and V. Morgan.
1993	J. W. Clark; vegetation survey by T. Dargie and I. Crawford (Dargie 1993); R. N. Evans & P. M. Hollingsworth (Hollingsworth et al. 1996).
1994	Scottish Natural Heritage Loch Survey (*Potamogeton* and charophyte records).
1995	C. J. Cadbury (Cadbury 1996); F. Horsman; L. Kinnes & P .S. Lusby (rare species survey).
1996	S. Henderson (Henderson 1996); Mrs K. Thorne.
1997	A. V. & D. A. Pearman, C. D. Preston & A. Walker; L. Farrell.
1998	C. J. Cadbury & N. Cowie (Cadbury & Cowie 1998); J. W. Clark; S. Phillips.
1999	L. Farrell and the Natural History and Antiquarian Society of Mid Argyll; C. Geddes & A. G. Payne.

The table summarises those visits which have produced records which are available to us. In addition K. A. H. and B. K. Cassels have spent many holidays here, as have P. F. and M. E. Braithwaite. For pre-1980 records, 'BRC' indicates that record cards are held at the Biological Records Centre, Monks Wood; 'Card Index' that records are on the card index started by Mrs J. W. Clark and held by the BSBI vice-county recorder.

We do not have exact dates for visits or records by Norwich Coastal Ecology Reseach Station (1960+), M. McCallum Webster and Mrs J. Stewart.

CHANGES IN THE FLORA

Although there are a few plant records from Coll and Tiree from the mid 18th century onwards, Macvicar's papers (1897a, 1897b, 1898) provide the first detailed accounts of the flora which provide a baseline against which change can be measured. However, the descriptions of the landscape and flora provided by earlier authors highlight just those features which are the main points of interest to the botanist today. Were Dr Johnson to revisit Coll today he would certainly find that, unlike his beloved London, it is still recognisable as the place he knew 200 years ago.

The major changes since the 1890s and 1930s have been the decline of arable weeds. The reduction in ploughed land has already been noted, and there is evidence that this has been accompanied by the decline of weeds such as *Agrostemma githago* (extinct), *Anagallis arvensis, Anchusa arvensis, Atriplex patula, Chrysanthemum segetum, Fumaria bastardii* and perhaps other *Fumaria* species, *Papaver dubium, Raphanus raphanistrum* and *Sinapis arvensis*. A number of other species which appear to have declined may have previously been sown in agricultural seed-mixes. These include *Alopecurus pratensis, Medicago lupulina, Trifolium dubium* and *Vicia sativa*.

It is difficult to point to other changes in the flora of the two larger islands (Gunna has not been well-recorded recently, and we cannot attempt to identify any changes there). The flora of Coll and Tiree had certainly been much modified before the islands were visited by botanists, with grazing being a particularly significant factor. However, the flora appears to have reached equilibrium or to be changing only very gradually. Some individual species may have declined, although many examples of apparent decline might be explained by earlier misidentifications or recent under-recording. Plants which may have declined on one or both islands include some grassland and heathland species (*Ajuga pyramidalis, Conopodium majus, Deschampsia flexuosa, Huperzia selago, Pyrola media, P. minor, Sagina subulata, Veronica serpyllifolia*), wetland species (*Hypericum tetrapterum, Lythrum salicaria, Potamogeton coloratus, Valeriana officinalis*), woody species (*Betula pubescens, Corylus avellana, Lonicera periclymenum, Prunus spinosa, Rosa* spp., *Salix aurita*), species of rocks and cliff ledges (*Silene dioica, Stachys sylvatica, Teucrium scorodonia*) and the coastal *Salsola kali*. Specific searches for individual species are needed to establish whether these plants have really declined or whether they have simply been overlooked. It is frustrating that in preparing this flora hundreds of miles from Tiree and Coll, we have been unable to undertake this additional fieldwork.

A total of 113 alien taxa (103 species and 10 hybrids) are now recorded from the islands. Two of these, *Papaver argemone* and *P. rhoeas*, are known solely from Macvicar's records. Only 35 of the remaining 111 were reported by Heslop Harrison, the remainder being later discoveries. Some of the aliens known in the 1930s were rare then and have virtually the same distribution today (*Ajuga reptans, Carduus crispus, Digitalis purpurea, Inula helenium, Lysimachia nummularia, Stellaria holostea*). *Aegopodium podagraria, Myrrhis odorata* and *Salix viminalis* were also rare then but are known from rather more localities now, whereas *Lolium multiflorum* and *Tanacetum vulgare* appear to have declined and *Conringia orientalis, Mentha spicata, Spergularia rubra, Torilis japonica* and *Veronica polita* have not been seen since the 1941 Flora was published.

Although many more aliens have been recorded since 1941, aliens still have a negligible ecological impact on the islands. In part, this is because over half of the species which we regard as alien on Coll and Tiree are native elsewhere in Britain. This high proportion probably reflects the fact that such aliens are easier to identify on islands than on the mainland. The species which are native in Britain tend to be rare as aliens on the islands (perhaps we would not recognise them as aliens if they were commoner). Many of the species which are alien to Britain as a whole are known from the islands as casuals, as weeds of cultivated land, walls or waste ground, or as planted trees or shrubs restricted to shelter belts or the few areas of planted woodland. The remainder tend to be naturalised in the wild in only one or two localities. Only a single alien, *Matricaria discoidea*, is frequent throughout the islands. This species was known to Heslop Harrison from several sites on Coll and has now spread to Gunna and Tiree. As a species of disturbed ground it has little impact on the native flora.

In summary, there is little evidence for marked changes in the last 100 years. Arable cultivation has decreased and the associated weeds have declined with it. There has been a turnover of alien species, with some being lost and rather more being recorded for the first time, but very few aliens have become widespread in the islands and none have succeeded in spreading widely into semi-natural habitats.

EXPLANATION OF THE SPECIES LIST

Source of records

Many of the records available from the islands were summarised on a card index started by Mrs J. W. Clark, and continued by Dr A. Walker, and this was maintained until 1990. Records from all sources up to 1999 have been incorporated into the database at the Biological Records Centre, Monks Wood, from which this flora has been prepared. An attempt has been made to include new 10km square data in the NVC survey of Tiree (Dargie 1993), but quite a few records that are new to the islands remain to be confirmed. We have looked for herbarium specimens where these were needed to solve particular problems, but we have been unable to look systematically through the entire collections at **BM** and other herbaria.

We have summarised records on the basis of 10km squares. For the *Atlas of the British Flora* (Perring & Walters 1962) an attempt was made to assign the records in Macvicar (1898) and Heslop Harrison *et al.* (1941) into this framework and the results are by and large acceptable. We have corrected obvious errors, but there are probably a few exaggerations in the database – for instance *Lolium multiflorum* is entered for T 94,04; C 15,25,26 on the strength of an entry in Heslop Harrison "an escape from cultivation in Coll and Tiree".

Coverage

Although Coll and Tiree have both been visited by BSBI meetings and other botanists in recent years, only a few brief visits have been made to Gunna and there has been little work on critical genera on this small island.

Recording coverage of the islands' habitats has been slightly uneven. Aquatic and saltmarsh plants have benefited from special surveys, and records of machair and strand-line plants seem quite adequate. However, moorland plants seem to have been under-recorded since Heslop Harrison's day, and this is also the case with woody plants on Coll (there are very few on Tiree). More work needs to be done to establish whether this lack of records arises from under-recording or from increased grazing pressure. There are many records of Cyperaceae from Tiree (because of DAP's survey), and relatively few from Coll. Yet the habitats are not terribly dissimilar, and this indicates that this group has been overlooked on Coll.

Although areas under cultivation have declined, we are not sure that all opportunities to record these habitats since 1987 have been taken; certainly we were quickly able to add many records in 1997 from the very small areas under cultivation that we looked at.

There seems to be evidence of lack of visits early or late in the season; species such as *Cochlearia danica, Myosotis discolor, Ranunculus ficaria,* and some genera, including *Atriplex, Rosa* and *Salicornia* are relatively poorly covered. Aliens too have been recorded only spasmodically and unevenly, but this only mirrors experience elsewhere in Britain.

Treatment of doubtful records

All records have been examined in the context of other records from our islands, and the distribution of plants elsewhere in the Hebrides and on the west coast of Scotland. We have used square brackets to enclose entries for species which we regard as doubtfully or erroneously recorded from the islands. Our comments and interpretations are explained in the text. Assessing historical records on the basis of inadequate evidence clearly involves an element of subjectivity, but we hope we have taken a pragmatic line.

We have included an assessment of all species for which there are published records known to us. There are a number of unpublished records, all made since 1960, for species which are totally unlikely to occur and we have omitted these altogether. These amount to less than ten species.

Format of the Species List

Species are in alphabetical order, with nomenclature of species, subspecies and hybrids following Stace (1997) unless stated. Hybrids are listed by parent, also in alphabetical order. An asterisk means that the taxon is not considered native in these islands.

A 10km square summary distribution is provided for Tiree (T), Gunna (G) and Coll (C). All unbracketed 10km records were made between 1 January 1987 and 31 December 1999; records in round brackets were made before

1987 and not subsequently. The records by 10km square are from west to east. Tiree falls mainly within NL94 and NM04, with a very small part of NL93, and an even smaller area of NM05. Gunna has only 2 1km squares, but these are divided between NM05 and NM15, and all recent recorders have differentiated between the two. Coll covers parts of NM15, 25 and 26, with a tiny part of a single 1km square falling into NM16. 'All' means that the species has been recorded from 1987 onwards in all squares, viz:

E	J	P	U	Z
D	I	N	T	Y
C	H	M	S	X
B	G	L	R	W
A	F	K	Q	V

Figure 10

Labelling of tetrads (2 × 2 km squares) within a 10km square

T 93,94,04,05; G 05,15; C 15,16,25,26.

It is interesting that 77 taxa, all native species, have been recorded recently from all squares, bearing in mind the tiny areas of Tiree 05, Gunna and Coll 16.

Detailed records are cited in the sequence: habitat, locality, grid reference, recorder, year, determiner, herbarium abbreviation or literature reference. For many records only some of these details are available, but the fact that grid reference precedes date should prevent confusion between dates and those grid references which might be read as dates (e.g. 1960, the only 1km square which contains land in NM 16). The habitat details are drawn from our own limited knowledge, generously supplemented by the comments on Joan Clark's card index, and frequently from Heslop Harrison *et al.* (1941) and occasionally from Macvicar (1898). Where locations are cited, they are listed from west to east. Except in direct quotations, the spelling of place names follows the Ordnance Survey 1:25 000 Second Series maps (1978). We have included four or six figure grid references if these are available. Some grid references are given to tetrad (2 × 2km square) level, e.g. 26A is tetrad A in NM 26. For the letters used to label the tetrads, see Fig. 10. "Recent" in the text means on or after 1 January 1987. Dates are sometimes given as 1987+, meaning 1987 onwards, if the exact year is not known. Herbarium abbreviations are in bold type and follow Kent & Allen (1984). Literature references are cited in the normal way, except that Heslop Harrison *et al.* (1941) is abbreviated to HH.

Place names

Equating place names in the botanical literature with those which appear on current maps presents relatively few problems, despite changes in spelling over the years (e.g. Macvicar's Kenavara is the Ordnance Survey's Ceann a'Mhara). There are, however, a few names of botanical sites which may require explanation. 'Odhrasgair', a name on some of Macvicar's specimens, is on the E side of An Fhaodhail, Tiree; it is still signposted from the coast road at Baugh. Heslop Harrison's site Dun an t-Sithein lies between An Fhaodhail and Gott Bay, Tiree, and is shown on the map in his Flora (Heslop Harrison *et al.* 1941). Dairy Loch on Coll is shown on current maps as L. Airigh Meall Bhreide, though the former name is used on the island. We deduce from the map in Heslop Harrison *et al.* (1941) that Eilean nam Faoileag is the island SW of Eileanan na h-Aornan, at grid reference NM 255592. We have cited records from several homesteads on Coll which are not named on the 1:25 000 maps: these include Garden House, Uig (NM 166542), Tom nan Eun, between Uig and Acha (NM 176544), Achamore, SE of Arnabost (NM 214596, 'Arnabost Farm' on the map and in Heslop Harrison's Flora) and Craigdarroch, Arinagour (NM 224572). The site Beg a'Mhonaidh is a rocky area near Broadhills in W Coll, NM 15.

Abbreviations of recorders, determiners and literature sources

AAPS	A.A.P. Slack	CG	C. Geddes
AC	A. Currie	CJB	C.J. Bruxner
ACJ	A.C. Jermy	CJC	C.J. Cadbury
AD	A. Daly	CK	C. Kitchen
AGP	A.G. Payne	CNP	C.N. Page
AJS	A.J. Silverside	CW	C. West
AJW	A.J. Wilmott	CWM	C.W. Murray
ALP	A.L. Primavesi	DAP	D.A. Pearman
AMcGS	A.McG. Stirling	DC	D. Counsell
AOC	A.O. Chater	DCL	D.C. Lang
AP	A. Piggott	DJMcC	D.J. McCosh
AW	A. Walker	DJT	D.J. Tennant
BC	B. Coppins	DMM	D.M. Moore
BH	B. Harold	DRMcK	D.R. McKean
BHT	B.H. Thompson	EB	E. Beveridge
BKC	B.K. Cassels	EFW	E.F. Warburg
BR	B. Rae	EN	E. Nelmes
BSB	B.S. Brookes	FH	F. Horsman
BSBI	Botanical Society of the British Isles (Field Meeting)	GDK	G.D. Kitchener
		GT	G. Taylor
		HH	Heslop Harrison *et al.* (1941)
BTS	B.T. Styles		
CAS	C.A. Stace	HHH	Helena Heslop Harrison
CCH	C.C. Haworth		
CD	C. Dixon	HJN	H.J. Noltie
CDP	C.D. Preston	IAW	I.A. Williams
CEH	C.E. Hubbard	IC	I. Crawford

JB	J. Bevan	PFH	P.F. Hunt
JED	J.E. Dandy	PFY	P.F. Yeo
JF	J. Fryer	PJOT	P.J.O. Trist
JG	J. Grimshaw	PMB	P.M. Benoit
JHH	J. Heslop Harrison	PMH	P.M. Hollingsworth
JM	J. Mackay	PT	P. Taylor
JMI	J. MacIntosh	PW	P. Wormell
JPB	J.P. Bailey	RDM	R.D. Meikle
JPS	J.P. Savidge	RECF	R.E.C. Ferreira
JRA	J.R. Akeroyd	RHR	R.H. Roberts
JWC	J.W. Clark	RMH	R.M. Harley
JWHH	J.W. Heslop Harrison	RNE	R.N. Evans
KAHC	K.A.H. Cassels	RS	R. Scott
KNGM	K.N.G. Macleay	SDW	S.D. Webster
KPB	K.P. Bland	SH	S. Haywood
KT	K. Thorne	SJL	S.J. Leach
LF	L. Farrell	SMM	S.M. Macvicar
LG	L. Garrad	SNHLS	Scottish Natural
MARK	M.A.R. Kitchen		Heritage Loch Survey
MEB	M.E. Braithwaite	SP	S. Phillips
MGBH	M.G.B. Hughes	TCGR	T.C.G. Rich
MMcCW	M.McCallum Webster	TD	T. Dargie
NFS	N.F. Stewart	UKD	U.K. Duncan
NTHH	N.T.H. Holmes	VG	V. Gordon
PDS	P.D. Sell	WAC	W.A. Clark
PFB	P.F. Braithwaite		

Summary of taxa recorded

The number of taxa recorded from the three main islands are given in Table 10 (next page).

Table 10

Summary of taxa recorded from Tiree, Gunna and Coll

		Tiree	Gunna	Coll	Total
Vascular plants					
Native species and microspecies' aggregates*		411	229	449	475
Alien and probably alien species		50	1	89	103
Microspecies:	*Hieracium*	0	0	9	9
	Rubus	4	0	7	9
	Taraxacum	5	0	23	†24
Native hybrids		18	0	22	31
Alien hybrids		3	0	9	10
Charophytes					
Native species		8	0	7	9

* The microspecies' aggregates are Hieracium spp., Rubus fruticosus agg. and Taraxacum spp. Salicornia spp. are excluded from these figures as the genus occurs, but no species have been identified with certainty.

† includes one alien microspecies from Coll.

SPECIES LIST

Vascular plants

Acer pseudoplatanus   Sycamore   T (94),(04);C 15,25,26

Planted, but uncommonly, around hotels and houses. Not recorded by HH.

Achillea millefolium   Yarrow   All

Very common in a wide range of habitats. Hairy plants on dunes are var. *villosa*, noted by HH from Tiree and collected from Balephuil Bay, 945407, CDP, 1997, det. PDS, **CGE**.

Achillea ptarmica   Sneezewort   T 94,04; (G); C 15,25,26

Scattered throughout the islands in ditches and wet fields, but nowhere common.

Aegopodium podagraria   Ground-elder   T 94,(04); C 15,25,26

Rare around habitations, with only five records. Only recorded once by HH.

Agrostemma githago   Corncockle   C (26)

Described as "abundant in cornfields, Torastan, Gallanach, Cornaig" by HH, but not recorded since.

Agrostis canina sens. lat.   Velvet/Brown Bent   All

Fairly well distributed in many different habitats but with relatively few records. There are only five records of *A. canina sens. strict.* (Velvet Bent), all from wet areas, from T 93, 94; C 15, 26. *A. vinealis* (Brown Bent) has been recorded from a rock outcrop W of Breachacha Castle, 15, DAP, CDP *et al.*, 1997, and from 26, CDP & NFS, 1989.

Agrostis capillaris   Common Bent   All

Seemingly fairly common everywhere over a wide range of soils, but usually in dry habitats.

Agrostis gigantea   Black Bent   T 94

Rare; only recorded in cultivated ground SW of Balephuil, 960405, DAP & CDP, 1997, conf. CAS, **CGE**. Scattered in W Scotland, with the nearest records in Skye and Islay.

Agrostis stolonifera   Creeping Bent   All

Very common everywhere including saltmarshes, and abundant at the edge of some lochans influenced by gulls (e.g. pool S of L. a'Chrotha, 237589).

Aira caryophyllea   Silver Hair-grass   T (94),04; C 15,(25),26

Rare on shallow soil over rock outcrops and on dunes; recorded twice by HH, and on only a few occasions since. The recent records are: N of Balevullin, 960470, TD, 1993; Port Fada, 985480, TD, 1993; Balephetrish Hill, 015473, BSBI, 1990; between Carpach and Crossapol, 15, CDP & NFS, 1989; Ben Feall, 146548, DAP & CDP, 1997; NW of Arnabost, 26A, JWC, 1987; Lochan a'Bhaigh, 26L, JWC, 1987; Cornaigbeg, 235630, PFB, 1990; Sorisdale, 2763, PFB, 1990.

Aira praecox   Early Hair-grass   All

Common on thin soil over rock outcrops, dry banks, walls and dunes.

Ajuga pyramidalis   Pyramidal Bugle   C (15),(25),(26)

Found "in a few places" by Scott (1881) on his brief visit to Coll in 1879, reported from crags near Grishipoll, 25, and a gorge near Meall na h-Iolaire, 26, by Heslop Harrison (1939a) and described as "widespread on rock ledges on Coll" by HH. The only post-war records are: SW of Ben Hogh, 179578, KAHC, 1984; near L. an Duin, 25, AMcGS, 1959, and a single plant, BSBI, 1967; near Sorisdale, 26, AMcGS, 1959. The sparsity of recent records suggests that the species has decreased in frequency on the island. The Ben Hogh area was searched carefully in July 1997 by DAP, CDP *et al.* with no success, but it appeared suitable, though hard-grazed.

*****Ajuga reptans***   Bugle   C 25

Only recorded in a meadow and near a large rocky knoll near Arinagour by HH, and in a rough garden on knoll W of Craigdarroch, Arinagour, JWC, 1983 and BKC, 1998 (possibly one of HH's sites).

Alchemilla filicaulis subsp. ***filicaulis***   Hairy Lady's-mantle   C (26)

HH only "rare amongst rocks near Cornaig". There are records for Mull, Rum and Skye.

Alchemilla glabra   Smooth Lady's-mantle   T 94; C 15,25,26

Uncommon in wet long grass by roadsides and ungrazed cliff ledges. On Tiree recorded from W side of Ceann a'Mhara, 938411, DAP & CDP, 1997, with older records from L. Bhasapol and Barrapol. On Coll known from Ben Hogh, 179578, HJN, 1987; Arinagour, 224572, DAP & CDP, 1997; Gallanach, 218604, JWC, 1988; Claic, 254635, JWC, 1987.

*Alchemilla mollis   Garden Lady's-mantle   C 25

Recorded once as garden escape at Airidh Mhaoraich, Arinagour, 231569, AW, 1989.

[Alisma lanceolatum   Narrow-leaved Water-plantain

Macvicar (1897a, 1897b, 1898) recorded *A. plantago-aquatica* var. *lanceolatum* from a ditch at Cornaig, Tiree, det. A. Bennett. At that time *A. plantago-aquatica* and *A. lanceolatum* were not regarded as distinct species, but neither has subsequently been recorded from the island and it seems likely that the plant was a form of *Baldellia ranunculoides*. It would be an overstatement to say that a determination by Bennett is a sure sign of a misidentification, but he was not a reliable authority.]

*Allium porrum   Leek   C 26

Dump near Sorisdale, JWC & HJN, 1987.

Allium ursinum   Ramsons   T (94); C (25)

Recorded from sea gorges on Ceann a'Mhara, 94, by many recorders up to JWC, 1982. There is only one record from Coll, on the W shore of L. Eatharna, HH.

Allium vineale   Wild Onion   C (26)

The only record is from HH, "on a rock ledge west of Sorisdale", but it may be correct. *A. vineale* is very rare in the W of Scotland, but has been recorded from cliff scrub at several sites on Mull.

*Alnus glutinosa   Alder   C 15,25

At Acha, 1854, DAP & CDP, 1997, and occasional in woodland around Arinagour, 2257, DAP, CDP *et al.*, 1997.

*Alnus incana   Grey Alder   C 25

Planted W of Arinagour, 220573, BSB, 1988.

Alopecurus geniculatus   Marsh Foxtail   All

Very common in ditches and wet places.

Alopecurus pratensis   Meadow Foxtail   T 04; C (25),(26)

Rare, and possibly only as a relic of cultivation on roadsides and pastures. There is only one record from Tiree, and three from Coll, at least two of which are from roadsides.

Ammophila arenaria   Marram   All

Widespread and frequent behind all sandy beaches.

Anacamptis pyramidalis Pyramidal Orchid T (94),04; G 15; C 15,16,(25),26

Confined to dunes and machair grassland, and rare there. There are eight recent records: The Reef, 0144, BSBI, 1990, and 012450, CJC, 1995; Gunna, 15, JWC & HJN, 1987, and SP, 1998; Hogh Bay, 172575, PFB, 1987; Cliad, 1960, JWC, 1991; W of Arnabost, 26, JWC, 1987; Dun Morbhaidh, 2363, JWC, 1987.

Anagallis arvensis   Scarlet Pimpernel   T 93,94,04; C (15),(25),26

A rare weed of cultivated ground, with eight recent records.

Anagallis minima   Chaffweed   T (04); C (25)

This inconspicuous species was recorded by Macvicar on the shore near the landing pier on Tiree and by HH near Cliad on Coll. The only subsequent record is from 25, BSBI, 1967. There are scattered sites along the W coast of Scotland.

Anagallis tenella   Bog Pimpernel   All

Frequent everywhere in wet places; often most abundant on rocky banks near the upper edges of marshes.

Anchusa arvensis   Bugloss   T 94,04; C (15),(25),26

An uncommon weed of cultivated ground with only five recent records, including only one on Coll: arable field, Arnabost, 26, JWC, 1987.

Angelica sylvestris   Wild Angelica   All

Common not only in marshes but also on cliffs and islands in lakes.

Antennaria dioica   Mountain Everlasting   All except T 05, C 16

Not infrequent on dry, rocky, well-drained habitats, particularly on Coll. We have not seen the bright red forms found by HH on Coll. A very rare micromoth, *Levipalpus hepatariella*, found on this species is almost confined to Coll (Parsons 1984).

Anthemis cotula   Stinking Chamomile   T (94)

This arable weed has been recorded once from "a field gay with weeds", Balemartine village, BSBI, 1968 (Duncan 1968a,b). Rare in western Scotland, with only a few scattered records.

Anthoxanthum odoratum   Sweet Vernal-grass   All except C 16

The most frequent pasture grass, which is also common on cliffs.

Anthriscus sylvestris   Cow Parsley   T 93,94,04; G 15; C 15,25,26

Certainly a common umbellifer but it largely occurs around habitations, as noted by Macvicar and HH.

Anthyllis vulneraria   Kidney Vetch   All except C 16

Common on dunes and machair on all the islands. Subsp. *lapponica* is recorded only at Soy Gunna, 107519, CDP, 1989, det. JRA, **CGE**, but is probably more widespread. Material at **BM** collected from Tiree in 1951 was determined as subsp. *vulneraria* by J. Cullen.

Aphanes arvensis sens. lat.   Parsley-piert   T (93),(04)

Recorded from Ben Hynish, 93, AMcGS, 1982, and from near Baugh, 04, HH. Neither record gives any indication of habitat. There is one further record of the segregate *A. australis* (Slender Parsley-piert) from Vaul Bay area, 04, AMcGS, 1982, again with no details of habitat.

Apium inundatum   Lesser Marshwort   T 93,94,04; C 15,25,26

Widespread in shallow water at the edge of lochs and pools on Tiree; less common in similar habitats on Coll, with only one record from 25.

Apium nodiflorum   Fool's-water-cress   T 93,94,04

Scattered and not particularly common on Tiree by ditches and, less frequently, the sides of lochs near the coast. Not recorded from Coll. For a map of recent records, see Fig. 6.

*****Aquilegia vulgaris***   Columbine   C 26

Dump, Sorisdale, JWC, 1987.

Arabidopsis thaliana   Thale Cress   T (04); C 25

Presumably a weed of cultivation with only two known localities: Dun an t-Sithein, 04, HH; hotel garden, Arinagour, 25, JWC, 1983, **E**, and JWC, 1987.

Arabis hirsuta   Hairy Rock-cress   T 94,04; G 15; C 15,(25),26

Widespread but fairly local on sand dunes, but also recorded by HH for rocks and bank sides.

[***Arctium minus sens. str.***   Lesser Burdock

The only records for this taxon are all from HH or before, together with a 1982 record from West Hynish, 93. There are no vouchers and they must all be considered doubtful, as there are no confirmed records of this plant in Scotland.]

Arctium nemorosum   Wood Burdock   T 94,04; C 15,25,26

Fairly common, especially on tracksides amongst dunes. Frequently found on waste ground and around farms too. There are records of *A. minus sens. lat.* from T 93, G 15 and C 16 which would almost complete the distribution.

Arctostaphylos uva-ursi   Bearberry   C 25,26

Restricted to the drier knolls and slopes in *Calluna* moorland north and east of Arinagour, with most of the records from L. Fada, 25, and the Sorisdale area, 26.

Arenaria serpyllifolia   Thyme-leaved Sandwort   All except T 05; G 05

Quite common on dry banks and dunes throughout. All the records are almost certainly referable to subsp. *serpyllifolia*, although only records for C 15 and 25 were definitely identified as such.

Armeria maritima   Thrift   All

Very common on coastal rocks and saltmarshes throughout the islands.

Arrhenatherum elatius   False Oat-grass   All

Widespread, but almost entirely as a result of disturbance or cultivation, and thus usually in waste places. Neither variety has been recorded systematically but var. *bulbosum* was noted twice in 1997, at the Garden House, Uig, 15R, DAP & CDP, and at The Lodge, Arinagour, 15, DAP & CDP, and var. *elatius* N of Cliad, 2059, DAP, CDP & AW, 1997.

*****Artemisia absinthium**   Wormwood   T (04); C (26)

A weed in gardens at Balephetrish, 04, Urvaig, 04, and Sorisdale, 26.

Artemisia vulgaris   Mugwort   T 94,04,05; C (15),25,26

An occasional but locally common weed of arable fields and rarely of waste places.

Asplenium adiantum-nigrum   Black Spleenwort   T 93,94,04; G 05; C all

Occasional but widespread on rock crevices. Probably more common on Coll, as there is more suitable habitat.

Asplenium marinum   Sea Spleenwort   T 93,94,04; (G); C 15,25,(26)

Widespread on suitably shaded sea cliffs, and again commoner on Coll.

Asplenium ruta-muraria   Wall-rue   C 15,25,(26)

Only recently found on walls, with recent records from the Garden House, Uig, 15, DAP & CDP, 1997, and Arinagour, 25, DAP, CDP *et al.*, 1997. HH has records only from cliffs, at Crossapol, 15, and Ben Feall, 15.

Asplenium trichomanes   Maidenhair Spleenwort
                                               T 93,(94),04; G 15; C 15,25,26

Cliffs and quarries, uncommon. Subsp. *quadrivalens* is confirmed from T (93),(04); G 15; C 26 and all records probably relate to this taxon.

Aster tripolium   Sea Aster   T 04; C 15

Found in small quantities in saltmarshes on Tiree: Baugh, 028436, SJL, 1990; NE of Salum, 073493, SJL, 1990; Soa, 075471, SJL, 1990; Millton, 085475, SJL, 1990. HH also recorded it from An Fhaodhail, which is less saline now. On Coll the only site is at Caoles, 126527, SJL, 1989.

Astragalus danicus   Purple Milk-vetch   T 94

Found only on south-facing grassy slopes on Ceann a'Mhara where 200 plants were found by JWC in 1984 and 70 plants at 940411 by CWM in 1990.

Athyrium filix-femina   Lady-fern   T 93,94,04; G 05; C 15,25,26

Widespread on cliffs and ditch sides on all the islands.

Atriplex glabriuscula   Babington's Orache
                                               T (93),94,04,05; (G); C 15,16,(25),26

Common and widespread on sandy shores; the most widespread *Atriplex* species on the islands.

***Atriplex glabriuscula* × *longipes* (*A.* × *taschereaui*)**   Taschereau's Orache
                                                                         T 04

Sandy shore, Vaul Bay, 054486, CDP, 1997, det. JRA, **CGE**.

Atriplex glabriuscula* × *praecox   T 05

Urvaig, 075500, DAP & CDP, 1997, det. JRA, **CGE**.

Atriplex laciniata   Frosted Orache   T (94),04; C 15,26

Very rare and only recorded from five sites; present in very small quantity at the two sites where it was seen in 1997. Tiree: Hough Bay, 94, HH; Traigh Bhagh, 0043, CJC, 1977; Vaul Bay, 054486, CDP, 1997. Coll: Feall Bay, 143544, DAP, CDP *et al.*, 1997; NW of Arnabost, 26, BKC & KAHC, 1987. Macvicar (1898) describes it as "common on some sandy shores; Salum Bay, etc.".

Atriplex patula   Common Orache   T (94),04,05; G (15); C (15)

A weed of cultivation, with only three records since 1960: Millton, 077476, DAP & CDP, 1997; Urvaig, 05, DAP & CDP, 1997; Tom nan Eun, 15, JWC, 1984.

Atriplex praecox   Early Orache   C 25

Sandy shore SW of Arinagour, 221557, DAP & CDP, 1997, det. JRA, **CGE**.

Atriplex prostrata   Spear-leaved Orache   T 94,04; C (15),25,(26)

Scattered in saltmarshes, and rare with only six recent records.

*Avena strigosa   Bristle Oat   T (94), (04)

CJC noted this species apparently cultivated as a crop in arable at Balephuil, 94, in 1969 and as a weed in a haycrop there in 1977. It was also recorded from dunes at Balephetrish, 04, BSBI, 1968, **BM**.

Baldellia ranunculoides   Lesser Water-plantain   T 94,04; C all

Relatively frequent in shallow marshes, pools, streams and around loch edges, and in particular, ditches. For a map of recent records, see Fig. 6.

Bellis perennis   Daisy   All

Abundant everywhere except on the poorest soils.

Berula erecta   Lesser Water-parsnip   T 94,04; C 26

Rare other than in An Fhaodhail, 04, where it is frequent. The only other sites are: Crossapol Burn, 991429, BSBI, 1990; stream, Stuthan Kirkapol, 044472, BSBI, 1990; marsh, Cliad Bay, 207608, CDP & NFS, 1989. There are very few records of *B. erecta* north of the Highland Line.

Beta vulgaris subsp. ***maritima***   Sea Beet   T (04); G 05; C 15,26

On rocks by the shore, very rare. Baugh, 017438, MMcCW, pre 1987, 1 plant; Gunna, 05, BSBI, 1989; near Ben Feall, 142548, KAHC, 1987, and DAP & CDP, 1997; Dun Morbhaidh, 26, JWC, 1987, 1 plant. It was not recorded at all by HH, and in W Scotland there are scattered records only from Colonsay, Mull and Canna.

Betula pubescens   Downy Birch   C 15,25

A very rare native tree, recorded with localities from L. Fada, 2359, KPB, 1987; behind Craigdarroch, Arinagour, 25, KPB, 1987; The Lodge, Arinagour, 224572, CDP, DAP *et al.*, 1997; new pier, Arinagour, 2256, KPB, 1987. HH gives more localities (L. Cliad, L. Airigh Meall Bhreide, W side of L. Eatharna). Definitely native only at L. Fada.

Blechnum spicant   Hard-fern   T (94),04; G 05; C 15,25,26

Relatively rare on cliffs and walls on Tiree, becoming slightly more common on Coll east of Arinagour.

Blysmus rufus   Saltmarsh Flat-sedge   T 93,94,04; C 15,25,26

In most saltmarshes, and thus quite frequent in the east of Tiree. It was abundant on wet sand in the lower reaches of An Fhaodhail, 016443, CJC, 1973, but not recorded subsequently, following the installation of a sluice at the mouth of the river. It also occurs on the west side of two lochans in W Tiree, L. Bhasapol, 9647, DAP, 1990, and L. a'Phuill, 9442, DAP, 1990, more than a kilometre from the sea. Less common, because there is less suitable habitat, on Coll.

Bolboschoenus maritimus   Sea Club-rush   T 93,94,04; G 05; C 15,25,26

In most saltmarshes, and occasionally in quite small brackish pools in rocks along the coast. Usually present at its sites in small quantity, in contrast to *Blysmus rufus*. For a map of recent records, see Fig. 9.

*** *Borago officinalis***   Borage   C 15,25

An escape from gardens at Uig and Tom nan Eun, 15, and a roadside casual near Arnabost, 25.

Botrychium lunaria   Moonwort   T 94,04; C 15,(25),26

On fixed dunes and other grassy places. There have been very few recent localised records: Ceann a'Mhara, 94, SP, 1998; Clachan Mor, 9847, CWM, 1990; Balephetrish, 015483, BSBI, 1990; W of Port-na-Luing, 149519, CG & AGP, 1999; Crossapol dunes, 142535, CG & AGP, 1999.

Brachypodium sylvaticum   False Brome   T 93,(94); C 15,(25),(26)

Recorded by HH from cliff ledges in W Tiree and as local but fairly widespread on Coll, there are only two records since 1968: Ben Hynish, 93, BSBI, 1990; Ben Hogh, 15, HJN, 1987.

*** *Brassica napus***   Rape   T 93,94,04; C (25),26

A casual weed of cultivation, with a handful of records.

*** *Brassica rapa***   Turnip   T 93,94,04; C 15,25,26

Another weed of cultivation, with only a few records. Var. *briggsii* was recorded at Balemartine, BSBI, 1968, **BM**.

*__Briza media__   Quaking-grass   T (94),(04)

A very rare species and perhaps only a casual, only ever recorded from L. an Eilein, 94, BSBI, 1968, and JWC, 1982, and from Gott Bay near the Manse, 04, HH. Very rare indeed in western Scotland.

__Bromus commutatus__   Meadow Brome   T (93),94; C (26)

A very rare grass of improved pasture: Hynish, 982390, CJC, 1975, the only one of 33 ley crops sampled in which it was recorded; SW of Balephuil, 960405, DAP & CDP, 1997, conf. CAS, **CGE**; half mile W of Cornaigbeg, 26, UKD, 1967, det. CEH, **BM**. Duncan's specimen has been redetermined as *B. racemosus*, but we hesitate to add this species to the flora in opposition to Hubbard's determination. The two species are closely related and perhaps only subspecifically distinct (Stace 1997).

__Bromus hordeaceus__ subsp. __hordeaceus__   Common Soft-brome
                                                              All except G 05

Common in dunes, waste places and on arable land throughout the islands.

[__Bromus hordeaceus__ subsp. __thominei__   Sand Soft-brome

This subspecies has only been recorded once, from C 15 by the BSBI meeting in 1967. There are no voucher specimens and it may have been mistaken for *B.* × *pseudothominei*, as is the case elsewhere in Britain.]

[__Bromus lepidus__   Slender Soft-brome

Recorded from C 15 by the 1967 BSBI meeting, but as there is no voucher we have not accepted the record.]

__Cakile maritima__   Sea Rocket   T (93),94,04; G 15; C 15,26

Scattered throughout the islands on sandy beaches, but never particularly common, except at the eastern end of Traigh Bhagh, 018439, CJC, 1995, when it was very frequent in a pioneer community. There are seven post-1987 records for Tiree, one from Gunna and three for Coll.

__Callitriche hamulata sens. lat.__   Intermediate Water-starwort
                                                       T 94,04; C 15,16,(25),26

Relatively uncommon in acid ponds, swamps, streams, lochs and ditches. Only once recorded for 25 and 26. HH reported this species as "abundant and of a colossal size in the stream near Acha, Coll" but CDP & NFS were disappointed to find that although it was frequent in the Allt a'Mhuilinn, 186548, 1990, **CGE**, its size was unremarkable.

[__Callitriche hermaphroditica__   Autumnal Water-starwort

Recorded from L. an Eilein, T 94, by HH, and not seen since. This species occurs from scattered localities in the western Highlands and might be found on Tiree, but the genus is a difficult one and we have therefore rejected the record.]

[*Callitriche platycarpa*   Various-leaved Water-starwort
Once recorded from Tiree airport, T 94, VG, 1960, det. JPS. Confirmation of the presence of this species is required.]

Callitriche stagnalis   Common Water-starwort   All except T 05, C 16
Common and widespread in streams, ditches, pools and open muddy habitats on all the islands. *C. stagnalis sens. lat.* is recorded from C 16.

Calluna vulgaris   Heather   All
Common and widespread on moorlands everywhere.

Caltha palustris   Marsh-marigold   All except T 05
Very common everywhere at the edge of lochs, in ditches and marshes.

Calystegia pulchra   Hairy Bindweed   C 26
Well established in garden, Gallanach Farm, JWC, 1988.

Calystegia sepium subsp. *sepium*   Hedge Bindweed   C 25,(26)
There are only two records for this species, as introductions in gardens at Arinagour and Gallanach.

Calystegia silvatica   Large Bindweed   C (25)
Once recorded, without precise locality, VG, 1960.

Calystegia soldanella   Sea Bindweed   T 94,(04); C 15,26
A rare plant of dunes, only recorded from four localities: Traigh nan Gilean, 9341, BSBI, 1990; Heanish to Baugh, 04, BSBI, 1968; Traigh nan Siolag, 1152, CDP & NFS, 1989; near Gallanach, 214613, JWC, 1987. HH recorded it from the last two localities.

Campanula rotundifolia   Harebell, Bluebell   T 93,94,04; (G); C all
Well distributed and fairly common on banks, dunes and rock ledges. On Tiree almost confined to Ben Hynish and Ceann a'Mhara, but on Coll more frequent, especially in the east. Plants growing on rocks covered by blown sand on the S side of Ben Feall, 142546, DAP & CDP, 1997, **CGE**, have been determined as subsp. *montana* (*C. giesekiana auct. britt.*) by PDS.

Capsella bursa-pastoris   Shepherd's-purse   T 93,94,04; C all

Generally common in waste places and in arable fields.

Cardamine flexuosa   Wavy Bitter-cress   T (93),(94),04; C 15,25,26

Not particularly common in waste places, but in our experience more frequent as a garden weed than *C. hirsuta*. HH on the other hand describes it as a plant of rocky crevices and gorges on W Tiree and Coll.

Cardamine hirsuta   Hairy Bitter-cress   T (94),04; G 15; C (15),25,26

Scattered, and usually in gardens and waste places.

Cardamine pratensis   Cuckooflower   All

Very common in marshes and fields everywhere.

__Carduus crispus__   Welted Thistle   T 04

A plant of waste places only recorded from Scarinish, first by HH and then by DAP at 043448 in 1997.

__Carduus nutans__   Musk Thistle   C 26

Twice recorded: cemetery NE of Gallanach, 2160, JWC, 1998; by road SW of A'Chroic, 2262, CDP & NFS, 1989.

[**Carex appropinquata**   Fibrous Tussock-sedge

Recorded from Gunna by HH, but never confirmed. There is no suitable habitat on Gunna for this species. The only Scottish records are from the Borders.]

Carex arenaria   Sand Sedge   All except C 16

Widespread on all dunes and machair systems, sometimes reaching a considerable distance from the sea, such as at Barrapol, 9542.

[**Carex bigelowii**   Stiff Sedge

Recorded from C 25 by HH "on rocky ridges near Loch Ronard, Loch na Cloiche etc.; quite rare". Never seen again and presumably a mistake. Recorded from much higher ground in Mull, Ardnamurchan and Rum.]

Carex binervis   Green-ribbed Sedge   All

Frequent everywhere on dry, rocky and heathery slopes, and thus more common on Coll than Tiree where it is rare other than in the west

Carex caryophyllea   Spring-sedge   T 93,94,05

Rare on calcareous rocky slopes. On Tiree there are records from Ceann a'Mhara, HH and 9340, 9440, DAP, 1990, and Urvaig, 0750, DAP &

CDP, 1997. There is a further record, to be confirmed, from Ben Hynish, 93U, BSBI, 1990. The only records from Coll are from HH, "thinly spread over Coll", and should probably be regarded as errors.

[*Carex curta*   White Sedge

Recorded by HH at L. a'Mhill Aird, C 26, and not recorded again. Frequent in Scotland, but uncommon in the Hebrides.]

Carex diandra   Lesser Tussock-sedge   T 94,04

This species has long been known from a small lochan NE of Dun Beag, 076493, where it was recorded by HH, ACJ, 1984 and DAP, 1990. Here it grows with *Pilularia globulifera* and *Menyanthes trifoliata*. CJC has recorded this sedge from two further sites, a very wet bog along ditch near W shore of L. Bhasapol, 967467, 1987, and a very wet marsh at L. nam Braoileagan, 008463, 1983. The former site is one of the two sites on Tiree for *C. paniculata*, but we have accepted the record for the time being. The marsh at L. nam Braoileagan had been drained and the species apparently lost by 1995.

Carex dioica   Dioecious Sedge   T 93,94,04; C all

Common in flushes and lawns, with *C. hostiana* and *Eleocharis quinqueflora* in 41 1km squares on Tiree. Presumably as common on Coll, but much under-recorded.

Carex distans   Distant Sedge   All

Frequent in saltmarshes and in brackish pools all around Tiree, with the exception of the far south-west. Less common but widespread on Coll and Gunna.

Carex disticha   Brown Sedge   T 93,94,04; C 15,25

On Tiree this species is found in herb-rich meadows with such species as *Filipendula ulmaria*, and occasionally in ditches. So far about 15 widely scattered localities have been recorded, all near the coast, confirming its preference for a high pH. On Coll there are only two records: Totronald, 1657, DAP & CDP, 1997; Arinagour, 225577, SJL, 1989.

Carex echinata   Star Sedge   All

Common and well-distributed on moorlands and mires with no sandy influence.

Carex elata   Tufted-sedge   T (94)

Known only from L. Bhasapol, June 1940, WAC, det. EN, **BM**. We have seen the specimen, which is correctly identified. It bears WACs label, was determined by EN on 8th August 1940 and reported by Heslop Harrison *et al.* (1941), all suggesting that the record is genuine. The only other possibility is that it was confused with a voucher from another locality. The species is very rare north of Cumbria, although it has been found at the Black Lochs near Oban.

Carex extensa   Long-bracted Sedge   T 04; G 05; C 15,25,26

Relatively rare amongst coastal rocks. Only found in three sites on Tiree: Ringing Stone, 028487, BSBI, 1990; Dun Mor, 043493, SJL, 1990; Port Ban, 096478, SJL, 1990. Recorded from Gunna, and at least five sites on Coll.

Carex flacca   Glaucous Sedge   All

Well distributed and very common in almost all habitats, particularly on the machair, where it has sometimes been misidentified as *C. caryophyllea*.

Carex hirta   Hairy Sedge   T 93,94,04; C (15)

Very much a sedge of roadside banks and improved areas on Tiree, and even here only recorded from six 1km squares. The only record for Coll is an unlocalised record by BSBI, 1967.

Carex hostiana   Tawny Sedge   T all; C all

Found in flushes throughout Tiree and almost as frequently on Coll. Apparently not recorded from Gunna.

Carex hostiana × **viridula** subsp. **brachyrrhyncha**   T 04; C 25,26

This hybrid has been recorded from An Fhaodhail, 04, DAP, 1990; L. Cliad, 25, JWC, 1987, and L. a'Mhill Aird, 231609, JWC, 1987, both det. AOC, **E**; near Gallanach, 26, HJN, 1987, det. ACJ.

[**Carex laevigata**   Smooth-stalked Sedge

Recorded by HH from the Urvaig-Miodar area on Tiree. Never confirmed or refound, although found in small quantities in woodland all along the W coast of Scotland.]

Carex lasiocarpa   Slender Sedge   C 15,25,26

Locally not uncommon on Coll in swamps or shallow water at the edge of lochans, and occasionally spreading across the entire width of shallow lochs. Before the BSBI week in 1989 there were only four known sites, but by visiting each loch for aquatic plants this was increased to 33, all in 25 and 26 with the exception of one record for 15: N end of L. Fada, 196587, CDP, 1990. For a map of recent records, see Fig. 4.

Carex limosa   Bog-sedge   C 25,26

Rare, but now known from eight sites in eastern Coll, in shallow water at the edge of lochs, *Menyanthes* beds and in bays more or less overgrown by vegetation. Sometimes present as extensive stands, as at L. Feisdlum, 2458. For a map of recent records, see Fig. 4.

Carex nigra   Common Sedge   All

Common in all habitats on all the islands. The most widespread sedge, often in dense stands.

Carex otrubae   False Fox-sedge   All

A coastal sedge, sometimes in saltmarshes, but often in coastal turf and amongst rocks. Although it is recorded in every 10km square, it is only known from a total of 17 1km squares on Tiree, compared with 91 for *C. nigra*.

Carex ovalis   Oval Sedge   All except G 05

Widespread on tracks, disturbed peaty ground and occasionally in improved fields that have 'gone back', with *Iris pseudacorus* and *Juncus* species.

Carex panicea   Carnation Sedge   All

Very common and widespread in all terrestrial habitats.

Carex paniculata   Greater Tussock-sedge   T 94; C 26

On Tiree only found in marshes around L. Bhasapol, where it has been known since Macvicar's time. The most recent records are: W of loch, 967466, DAP, 1990; S of loch, 972465, DAP, 1990. It is recorded from one area on Coll: NW of Arnabost, 206601, 208601 and 207608, JWC, 1987.

Carex pilulifera   Pill Sedge   T 93,94,04; (G); C all

Scattered throughout Tiree, and more common on Coll, on dry, rocky ground, with heather. Probably under-recorded.

Carex pulicaris   Flea Sedge   All except G 05

Widespread in flushes with *C. dioica*, *C. hostiana* and *Eleocharis quinque-flora*.

[*Carex riparia*   Greater Pond-sedge

"Collected by our students in the Acha area", C 25, HH. What could he have mistaken for it? *C. riparia* is only known from a very few sites in Scotland, in the south.]

Carex rostrata   Bottle Sedge   T 93,94,04; C 15,25,26

Quite widespread in deeper lochs and ditches on Tiree; more frequent on Coll. For a map of recent records, see Fig. 7.

[***Carex sylvatica***   Wood-sedge

"On a grassy bankside near the cist between Miodar and Caoles", T 04, HH. Never confirmed from Tiree, but not particularly rare in woodland on Mull and other islands in the Inner Hebrides.]

[***Carex vesicaria***   Bladder Sedge

Recorded from a swamp at Kilkenneth, 945444, TD (Dargie 1993). This species is only recorded for the Hebrides from two localities on Mull and we do not accept this record without a voucher.]

Carex viridula   Yellow-sedge   All except G 15

Widely distributed in all wet habitats. The following subspecies have been recorded.

Subsp. *brachyrrhyncha*: Fairly frequent, often with subsp. *viridula* in bare stony habitats at the edge of small lochs. Occasional in ditches and in flushes with *C. hostiana* and others. Despite HH's comment that it is occasional on moorlands on Coll, there are recent records only for C 26. Jermy & Crabbe (1978) report no confirmed records from Mull. T 93,94,04; C (15),(25),26.

Subsp. *oedocarpa*: The most frequent of the subspecies, widespread and common in flushes, boggy fields and the edges of lochs. All except G 15.

Subsp. *viridula*: Slightly more common than subsp. *brachyrrhyncha* in the same habitats, particularly in bare stony or sandy grounds by lochs. Found in 23 1km squares on Tiree but there are only two records for Coll. It must be overlooked there. T all; C 15,25.

Catabrosa aquatica   Whorl-grass   All

Widespread on sandy beaches, usually where streams reach the sand. The common plant is var. *uniflora*, which is frequent in such habitats in north-west Scotland. Larger plants collected from a floating mass of vegetation in fresh water from a farm yard at Clachan Mor, 984477, SJL, 1990, **CGE**, were determined by PJOT as var. *grandiflora* Hack. ex Druce. There are specimens in **CGE** determined by PJOT as this variety from Caithness, Outer Hebrides and Shetland.

Catapodium marinum   Sea Fern-grass   T all; G 15; C 15,25,26

Not uncommon and usually on the harder areas of sand by the sea.

[*Catapodium rigidum*   Fern-grass

This has been recorded from similar habitats as *C. marinum* in T (93),(94),(04) almost certainly in error for that species. *C. rigidum* is known (perhaps as a casual) from the Outer Hebrides but is otherwise only recorded for Scotland on the east coast from Dundee southwards.]

Centaurea nigra   Common Knapweed   All

Frequent and well-distributed in pastures.

Centaurium erythraea   Common Centaury   All except T 05

Frequent and well-distributed on dry banks and dune slacks throughout.

Cerastium diffusum   Sea Mouse-ear   All

Common on all sandy soils throughout the islands.

Cerastium fontanum   Common Mouse-ear   All

Very common on sandy soils, in arable fields, and as a garden weed.

Cerastium glomeratum   Sticky Mouse-ear   T 93,(94),04; G 15; C 15,25,26

Fairly common as a weed of roadsides, gardens and cultivated fields.

Cerastium semidecandrum   Little Mouse-ear   C (15),26

This plant of dry open places on sandy soils has been recorded from Tiree by Vose et al. (1957) and by Dargie (1993). In the absence of a specimen we have rejected these records as possible errors for *C. diffusum* or *C. fontanum*. This species is very rare in the Hebrides, but might be expected on Tiree. There are three records from Coll: Breachacha area, 15, BSBI, 1967 and JWC, 1982; N of Cornaigbeg, 26, JWC, 1988.

* *Chamerion angustifolium*   Rosebay Willowherb   T (04); C 25,26

There is a record from Tiree, 04, AMcGS, 1959, but it has not been seen again. From Coll: behind Doctor's house, 217574, HJN, 1987; under heronry, L. Ghille-caluim, 257610, JWC, 1988. *C. angustifolium* is not common in W Scotland, and we assume that these are introductions.

Chenopodium album   Fat-hen   T 93,94,04; C 15,25,26

Widespread, with a few plants usually present wherever there is cultivated land. Records for the aggregate and the species are listed together.

Chrysanthemum segetum   Corn Marigold   T 94,04; C (15),(25),26

Described as "too common" in cultivated land by HH but now only found in abundance on recently cultivated machair; otherwise an infrequent weed of vegetable plots and gardens. Only one record from Coll since 1967: Gallanach Stackyard, 26, JWC, 1993.

Chrysosplenium oppositifolium   Opposite-leaved Golden-saxifrage   C (26)

Recorded as very rare in a sea-gorge near Eilean nam Faoileag, 26, HH and BSBI, 1967. Although the island is in 25, we have allocated this record to 26 as this is the 10km square in which it was recorded by the BSBI party. The species is not uncommon in the Inner Hebrides and on the west coast of Scotland.

* ***Cichorium intybus***   Chicory   T (04)

Only recorded once, in 1959.

Cirsium arvense   Creeping Thistle   All

Abundant throughout the islands. The distinctive var. *vestitum* grows on dunes at Balephuil Bay, 945407, CDP, 1997, det. PDS, **CGE**. Two other varieties recorded by HH have not been reported recently.

Cirsium palustre   Marsh Thistle   T 93,94,04; C all

Widespread on cliffs, pastures and moorland throughout the islands, but never very common and with less than 20 recent records.

Cirsium vulgare   Spear Thistle   All except G 05

More frequent than *C. palustre*, and widespread in all suitable habitats, especially those influenced by cultivation.

Cladium mariscus   Great Fen-sedge   C 25,26

Small stands in swamps and at the edge of lochs from just W of Arinagour right to the NE of Coll; occasionally present in larger stands. Often found flowering in 1989 and 1990. For a map of recent records, see Fig. 4.

* ***Claytonia sibirica***   Pink Purslane   C (15),(25)

Recorded for Acha, 15, beside a burn, and introduced from this population to Arinagour, 25.

Cochlearia danica   Danish Scurvygrass
T 93,94,04,(05); (G); C (15),16,(25),26

On rocks and by pools near the sea. Not very common, and only recorded three times by SJL in his saltmarsh study. However, that may have taken place too late in the year to detect some populations.

Cochlearia officinalis sens. lat.   Common Scurvygrass   All

Widespread in saltmarshes, and at the back of beaches on all the islands. There are older records from the 1960s for the critical *C. scotica* from T (94),(04), but for the moment it seems better to include all records under *C. officinalis sens. lat.*

Coeloglossum viride   Frog Orchid   T 94,04; G 15; C 15,(25),26

Dry grassy banks on machair. Either the grazing regime has changed, or recorders have been at the wrong time of year, or simply missed it, but there are few recent records other than five from The Reef area, 94 and 04, CJC, 1995.

***Coeloglossum viride* × *Dactylorhiza fuchsii* (× *Dactyloglossum mixtum*)**
                                                                    C (15)

One plant near Breachacha, 15, JHH, 1947, conf. HWP (J. Heslop Harrison 1949).

Conium maculatum   Hemlock   T 93,94,04; C 15,25,26

Never very common, this species is restricted to sites around houses and farm buildings.

Conopodium majus   Pignut   T (04); C (15),(25),26

A very rare plant of unimproved pastures. HH recorded it from Baugh, 04, Arinagour, 15, and Arnabost, 15. The BSBI meetings in 1967 and 1968 recorded it from all squares on Coll, but the only records since then are from W of Caolas-an-eilean, 210556, JWC, 1984, and fields at Gallanach, 26, JWC, 1988.

* ***Conringia orientalis***   Hare's-ear Mustard   T (04)

A casual near the pier, Gott Bay, HH.

Corylus avellana   Hazel   C 25,(26)

HH describes this as occurring "sparingly on nearly every cliff ledge from Loch Fada to the eastern shores of Loch Cliad on Coll". There are a few records from 25, mainly around Arinagour, but also W of Caolas-an-eilean, JWC, 1984. From 26 the only localised record is: S of Bousd, BC, 1983.

* ***Cotoneaster horizontalis***   Wall Cotoneaster   C 25

Several self-sown plants by unoccupied houses W of Arinagour, 221573, DAP, CDP *et al.*, 1997, det. JF, **CGE**.

__Cotoneaster simonsii__ Himalayan Cotoneaster C 25

Wood E of The Lodge, Arinagour, 219573, DAP, CDP *et al.*, 1997, det. JF, **CGE**.

[*Crambe maritima* Sea-kale

MacCulloch's (1819) record of *Crambe maritima* "in abundance along the sandy shores on the western side" of Coll has not been accepted by later authors. The species is very rare in the Hebrides although it does occur on North Uist. The record from Coll may indeed be an error for *Cakile maritima*, though the fact that MacCulloch (1824) later referred to "sea kale in its native state" on the island suggests that he was familiar with the vegetable.]

__Crataegus monogyna__ Hawthorn T 94; C (15),25

Planted as a windbreak below Ben Hynish, 970406, TD, 1993; L. an Eilein, 991453, TD, 1993. The only recent record from Coll is from The Lodge, Arinagour, 25, DAP, CDP *et al.*, 1997.

__Crepis capillaris__ Smooth Hawk's-beard T 94,04,05; C 15,25,26

Widespread on the machair and on roadsides throughout the islands. Vars *agrestis*, *capillaris* and *glandulosa* have all been recorded.

__Crocosmia aurea__ × *__pottsii (C.__* × *__crocosmiiflora)__* Montbretia C 15,25,26

First recorded in 1967, this is now naturalised in at least three places.

[*Cryptogramma crispa* Parsley Fern

Recorded only by the BSBI visit in 1967, from C 25. Oddly this discovery is not included in the reports of the meeting (Duncan 1968a,b). NFS (pers. comm.) once investigated a report of this species for Jura, which turned out to be young *Dryopteris aemula*.]

__Cymbalaria muralis__ Ivy-leaved Toadflax C (15),25,26

A few records from walls.

__Cynosurus cristatus__ Crested Dog's-tail All

Widespread and very frequent in all grasslands on cliffs and machair. HH recorded viviparous specimens from Arinagour, 25.

__Dactylis glomerata__ Cock's-foot T 93,94,04; C 15,25,26

Recorded by HH as very rare in both Tiree and Coll, but there are quite a few recent records. There is no obvious explanation for the apparent increase of this species.

Dactylorhiza

J. W. Heslop Harrison paid particular attention to the taxonomically notorious *Dactylorhiza* species and their hybrids, which were then still placed in the genus *Orchis* (cf Heslop Harrison 1939b). His son J. Heslop Harrison (1949) published detailed morphometric and ecological studies based on populations in the Hebrides, including some on Coll and Tiree. Although orchids attracted much attention during the BSBI meetings in 1989 and 1990 relatively few records of the infraspecific taxa and hybrids resulted, probably because only one member of the party, AMcGS, had any expert knowledge of the group. The infraspecific taxonomy of the following species follows Sell & Murrell (1996).

Dactylorhiza fuchsii　　　　Common Spotted-orchid　　All except C 16

Frequent in moist meadows and pastures on the more base-rich soils in all three islands. HH implied that all the material was referable to subsp. *hebridensis* (*Orchis maculata* var. *hebridensis*), and records of this taxon are available for T 04; C (15), (26). Subsp. *okellyi* was recorded on machair at the extreme E end of Traigh Mhor, T 04, by DCL in 1973. Few of the available records refer unambiguously to the type subspecies, but there is a specimen from wet, base-rich soils at Caoles, 1252, JWC, 1986, **E**. However, J. Heslop Harrison (1968) suggested that the characters of these subspecies overlapped to such an extent that an individual could not be identified without a knowledge of its geographical origin.

***Dactylorhiza fuchsii* × *incarnata* (*D.* × *kerneriorum*)**　　　C (15),(26)

The first record was from a marsh between Meall na h-Iolaire and Sorisdale, 26, HH, the basis of Heslop Harrison's description of *Orchis* × *variabilis*. In 1947 J. Heslop Harrison (1949) recorded the hybrid at Grishipoll, 15 (one plant), Bousd, 26 (two plants) and Sorisdale, 26 (three or more plants), conf. HWP.

***Dactylorhiza fuchsii* × *maculata* (*D.* × *transiens*)**　　　T 94,04; C (15)

Recorded from: Traigh Bail'-a-mhuilinn, 94, AMcGS, 1990; between Gott Manse and Dun an t-Sithein, 04, JHH, 1947; Balephetrish, 04, CWM & AW, 1990; near Acha Mill, 15, HH; near Caoles, 15, UKD, 1967, det. PFH. J.W. Heslop Harrison described his material as *Orchis* × *corylensis*. JHH's record was based on two large hybrid swarms on pastures reclaimed by drainage from *Calluna* heath (J. Heslop Harrison 1949).

***Dactylorhiza fuchsii* × *purpurella* (*D.* × *venusta*)**　　　T 04; C (15),(25),(26)

There is a single record from Tiree: The Reef, 04, AMcGS, 1990. On Coll the hybrid was recorded from a little marsh between Sorisdale and Bousd,

26, HH and noted by JHH in 1947 at Clabhach, 15 (two plants), Arinagour, 25 (hybrid colony on disturbed ground) and Sorisdale, 26 (two or three plants), conf. HWP.

Dactylorhiza fuchsii × *Gymnadenia conopsea* (× *Dactylodenia st-quintinii)*
C (15),(26)

Recorded by HH from Ceann Fasachd, 15, and described by JWHH as × *Orchigymnadenia cookei* after R.B. Cooke of the Newcastle team. In 1947 JHH found two plants at Ballyhaugh, 15, and three or more between A'Chroic and Cornaigbeg, 26, conf. HWP.

Dactylorhiza incarnata   Early Marsh-orchid   All except T 05
Frequent in the damper areas of sand dunes and machair, rarer in calcareous areas by lochs and by streams in moorland. Subsp. *coccinea* is recorded from T 93,94,04; G 15; C 15,16,26 and subsp. *incarnata* from T 94,04; C (15),26.

Dactylorhiza incarnata × *maculata (D.* × *carnea)*   T (04); C (15)
Recorded by HH at Scarinish Moor, 04, and near Breachacha, 15.

Dactylorhiza incarnata × *purpurella (D.* × *latirella)*   C (26)
Recorded by HH with the parents on the S side of Sorisdale Bay, 26.

Dactylorhiza maculata subsp. *ericetorum*   Heath Spotted-orchid
T 93,94,04,(05); G 05,15; C all

Frequent on moist, peaty moorland.

Dactylorhiza maculata × *purpurella (D.* × *formosa)*   T (04); C (26)
UKD recorded this hybrid from the Caoles area, 04, 1968, det. PFH. Both HH and UKD (1967, **K**) found it near Cornaigbeg, 26, the latter from a field known locally as Cornaig meadow which was fenced from sheep.

[*Dactylorhiza majalis* subsp. *occidentalis*   Western Marsh-orchid
Recorded by HH near Carachan, T 94, and in a little marshy hollow near Sorisdale, C 26. The records require confirmation in view of the very restricted distribution of this subspecies in Scotland.]

Dactylorhiza purpurella   Northern Marsh-orchid
T (93),94,04; G 15; C (15),16,(25),26

Damp places by the coast, by lochs and in moorland. JHH regarded it as the least abundant *Dactylorhiza* species on these islands, and Cadbury (1995) noted that it is surprisingly scarce on Tiree.

Dactylorhiza traunsteineri   Narrow-leaved Marsh-orchid   T (04)

Discovered in 1983 by CJC, who noted 25 flowering spikes in damp turf by L. nam Braoileagan, 007463, conf. DJT, associated with *Caltha palustris, D. fuchsii, Equisetum fluviatile, E. palustre* and *Eriophorum angustifolium.* Not seen by CJC in 1995 or 1998. One of very few populations in western Scotland (Stewart *et al.* 1994).

Danthonia decumbens   Heath-grass   All

Frequent on grassy areas on moors and amongst rocks on all the islands.

Daucus carota   Wild Carrot   All except G 05

Frequent in turf on rocky coasts, on dunes and machair and other grassy places. PDS considers that dwarf plants collected from blown sand on a cliff slope on the S side of Ben Feall, 142546, DAP & CDP, 1997, **CGE**, must be referable to subsp. *gummifer*, although they are not as typical as populations from SW England.

Deschampsia cespitosa   Tufted Hair-grass   T 93,94,04; C 25,26

Not particularly common on either island, with only seven recent records.

Deschampsia flexuosa   Wavy Hair-grass   T (94),(04); G 05; C 15,25,26

Rare in dry places on rocks, with no recent record for Tiree. Slightly more common on Coll, but even here only a few records. Abundant, Soa, 1551, JWC, 1987.

Deschampsia setacea   Bog Hair-grass   T 04; C 25,26

A rare grass, usually found in shallow water at the stony edges of acidic lochans. Very rare on Tiree, recently recorded only from dried-out bog near L. nan Ob, 0347, CDP & NFS, 1990, det. PJOT, **CGE**. Not uncommon in NE Coll, with nine sites.

*****Digitalis purpurea***   Foxglove   T (04); C 25

Extremely rare. Recorded by HH from near Dun an t-Sithein, 04, and near Arinagour, 25, on a site which is now a garden. There are two more recent records from outside gardens in this area.

Draba incana   Hoary Whitlowgrass   T 94,04; C 15,(25),26

A rare plant with only two recent records from sand dunes on Tiree: near L. a'Phuill, 9542, JWC, 1990; The Reef, 0144, BSBI, 1990. It was also abundant on the cracked concrete base of a disused aircraft hanger on The Reef, 008456, CJC, 1973, and a disused runway in the same area, 005453, CJC, 1983. There are five recent records from sand dunes on Coll.

Drosera anglica   Great Sundew   C (25),26

The rarest of the three sundews, with no confirmed records in C 25 other than "beside a small loch about a mile and a half from Aranagour" (Scott 1881). In the NE of Coll there are records from pools E of L. nam Breac Mora, 256616, CDP & NFS, 1989; shore of L. Ronard, 237608, NFS, 1990; L. a'Mhill Aird, 26, AD, 1989.

Drosera intermedia   Oblong-leaved Sundew   T 94,04; C 15,25,26

In flushes with *Pinguicula* spp., amongst *Sphagnum* or at the edge of peaty lochs. Less frequent on moorland than *D. rotundifolia* but forming conspicuous red bands around some lochs in E Coll. For a map of recent records, see Fig. 5.

Drosera rotundifolia   Round-leaved Sundew   T 93,94,04; C all

Well distributed, but nowhere common, on moorland.

Dryopteris aemula   Hay-scented Buckler-fern   C 15,25,26

Very local, but not infrequent in gullies on Coll, from W of Caolas-an-eilean, 210556, to Sorisdale, 26, with western outliers S of Uig, 165529, DAP & CDP, 1997, and at Grishipoll, 189593, JWC, 1984.

Dryopteris affinis   Scaly Male-fern   T 94,(04); C 15,25,26

The species is rare in W Tiree (Ceann a'Mhara and Beinn Hough) and occasional on Coll, again in rock crevices and sheltered cliffs. Three subspecies have been recorded.

Subsp. *affinis*: Ceann a'Mhara, 936402, AMcGS, 1990, **GLAM**.

Subsp. *borreri*: Uig, 168544, DAP & CDP, 1997, det. AP, **CGE**; Caolas-an-eilean, 220555, DAP, CDP *et al.*, 1997, det. AP, **CGE**.

Subsp. *cambrensis*: S of L. Ronard, 204553, BSB, 1988.

[Dryopteris carthusiana   Narrow Buckler-fern

Only recorded by HH on an island in L. Ghille-caluim, C 26. Rare in wet woodlands and in mires on many of the islands in the Inner and Outer Hebrides, but unlikely on a rocky islet.]

Dryopteris dilatata   Broad Buckler-fern   T (93),94,04; C 15,25,26

Not as widespread as *D. filix-mas*, but again, found in sheltered places amongst rocks. Recorded from about 15 recent localities.

Dryopteris filix-mas   Male-fern   T 93,94,(04); G 05; C 15,25,(26)

The most widespread fern on Coll and Tiree, found in a variety of habitats, but most frequently amongst rocks.

Elatine hexandra   Six-stamened Waterwort   T 04

Confined to scattered localities on E Tiree. It was discovered by AAS in 1982 on the margins of a small lochan, L. an t-Sleibh Dheirg, 073483, growing with *Pilularia globulifera*, and it has been confirmed there several times since. Subsequently found in: pool NE of L. nan Ob, 031485, NFS, 1990; L. an Fhaing, 040492, BSBI, 1990; lochan near L. an t-Sleibh Dheirg, 075484, CDP & NFS, 1989; L. an Air, 091473, BSBI, 1990.

Eleocharis multicaulis   Many-stalked Spike-rush   All except G 15; C 16

Widespread and frequent in all acid and boggy habitats, especially on wet moorlands and the shallow margins of acidic lochs. For a map of recent records, see Fig. 7.

Eleocharis palustris   Common Spike-rush   All

More widespread and frequent than *E. multicaulis*, being distributed around the coasts and in less acidic waters inland. For a map of recent records, see Fig. 7.

Eleocharis quinqueflora   Few-flowered Spike-rush   All except G

Widespread in the more basic flushes and in saltmarshes, with *C. hostiana* and *C. dioica* but less common than both. Much less frequently recorded than *E. multicaulis*, but that is surely solely because it is overlooked. Detailed recording on Tiree showed they were equally common.

Eleocharis uniglumis   Slender Spike-rush   T all; (G); C all

In only a few places on Tiree (13 1km squares) in saltmarshes, or amongst rocks in the spray zone. CJC has noted it on wet sand, damp slacks, remnants of saltmarsh and poor fen mires on The Reef and by An Fhaodhail, including a possible hybrid swarm with *E. palustris* at 019443 (Cadbury 1996). Apparently rare on Coll, with only six recent records.

Eleogiton fluitans   Floating Club-rush   T 93,94,04; (G); C 15,25,26

Frequent and widespread on Tiree and Coll, not only in peaty swamps and lochans but also in pools at the edge of sand dunes, and in some ditches. For a map of recent records, see Fig. 7.

Elytrigia juncea   Sand Couch   All except C 16

Widespread on the mobile dunes, but not extending to the machair behind.

Elytrigia repens   Common Couch   T 94,04; (G); C 15,25,26

Apparently not rare in waste places, road verges and shingle but few records in the database (10). Subsp. *repens* var. *aristata* and subsp. *repens* var. *repens* have each been recorded just once: both from Garden House, Uig, 166542, DAP & CDP, 1997.

Empetrum nigrum subsp. **nigrum**   Crowberry   (G); C 15,25,26

"Common and well distributed on rocky moorlands on Coll, Gunna and Ornsay" according to HH, but there are only nine recent records for the subspecies, or for *E. nigrum sens. lat.*, from coastal heath and moorland.

[**Epilobium alsinifolium**   Chickweed Willowherb

Mapped for C 15 in Stewart *et al.* (1994) as a result of a wrong grid reference for a site in Mull.]

__Epilobium brunnescens__   New Zealand Willowherb   C 15,25,26

First recorded in 1984, there are three recent records from open waste ground: dunes SW of Carpach, 152532, BSB, 1988; C 25, BSB, 1988; NW of Gallanach, 205612, BSB, 1988.

__Epilobium ciliatum__   American Willowherb   T 94,04; C 25,(26)

This North American alien is now widespread in the British Isles. HH recorded it from a dried-up loch in Gallanach dunes, 26, and also from South Uist, Outer Hebrides (Heslop Harrison 1941b), suggesting that it was "an American species and may not be a colonist in the Hebrides". These records were made at a time when the species was otherwise restricted to southern Britain, and they have not been accepted by later botanists (Preston 1989). The first acceptable record from Tiree was made in 1982 and from Coll in 1985. Now recorded from a few gardens and a shelterbelt.

__Epilobium hirsutum__   Great Willowherb   T 93,(94),04

All records appear to be from gardens, where it has presumably been introduced with cultivated plants.

Epilobium montanum   Broad-leaved Willowherb
                                    T (93),(94),04; (G); C 15,25,26

Seemingly rare amongst rocks and as a garden weed.

Epilobium obscurum   Short-fruited Willowherb
                                    T (94),(04); (G); C 15,25,26

There are only four recent records for this species which HH described as "being thinly distributed in wet places in all the islands". On the other hand TD recorded it for Tiree from over 30 sites in 1993. But he had very few sites for *E. palustre* or *E. parviflorum* and we have therefore omitted these records until confirmed. *E. obscurum* is frequent in N Scotland.

Epilobium palustre   Marsh Willowherb   All

Widespread and frequent in all marshes, flushes and ditches.

Epilobium palustre × *parviflorum (E.* × *rivulare)*   T 04

With *E. palustre* in *Hippuris vulgaris* swamp, An Fhaodhail, 017445, CDP & NFS, 1989, det. GDK, **CGE**.

Epilobium parviflorum   Hoary Willowherb
                              T (93),94,04; G 05,15; C 15,25,26

Widespread and fairly frequent in wet places.

[*Epipactis palustris*   Marsh Helleborine

Machair Mhor, C 1757, LF, 1996. A single vegetative plant, believed by LF to be this species but not seen subsequently despite searching. This is an extremely rare plant in Scotland, with records from the west only from Colonsay and Islay.]

Equisetum arvense   Field Horsetail   T all; C 15,25,26

Very common in ruderal habitats throughout.

Equisetum arvense × *fluviatile (E.* × *litorale)*   Shore Horsetail   C 25

Moist ditch by wood S of road, The Lodge, Arinagour, 220573, DAP, CDP *et al.*, 1997, **CGE**.

Equisetum fluviatile   Water Horsetail   T 93,94,04; C all

Widespread and common in standing waters throughout the islands. In 1990 all the emergent stems at L. a'Gharbh-airde, 2156, were eaten off 15 cm above water level, perhaps by a pair of geese which reared a gosling here. For a map of recent records, see Fig. 7.

Equisetum hyemale × *variegatum (E.* × *trachyodon)*
                              Mackay's Horsetail   C 15

Dune slack at Crossapol, 143534, CG & AGP, det. CD, 1999; dunes, W of Breachacha, 149538, HJN, det. CNP, 1987, **E**. These confirm an earlier record of HH, "just behind the dunes, south west of the Round House". Neither of the parents occur on Coll.

Equisetum palustre   Marsh Horsetail   T 93,94,04; (G); C 15,25,26

Widespread and common in wet places in fields, bogs and around lochs.

Equisetum sylvaticum   Wood Horsetail   C 25,26

Very rare and only recorded from a wood at Arinagour and on heathy ground near Sorisdale: The Lodge, Arinagour, 219573 and 220573, DAP, CDP *et al.*, 1997; cliffs SW of Sorisdale, 26, AW, 1989.

Erica cinerea   Bell Heather   All except T 05

Widespread and frequent over all the islands.

Erica tetralix   Cross-leaved Heath   All except T 05

Common and widespread, especially on the moorlands.

* ***Erinus alpinus***   Fairy Foxglove   C 25

Originally planted but now well naturalised on the wall of Craigdarroch, Arinagour, 224572, CDP & NFS, 1989 and DAP, CDP *et al.*, 1997.

Eriocaulon aquaticum   Pipewort   C 25,26

One of the celebrated rarities of Coll, first found by MacCulloch (1819) "growing in some of the central lakes in company with *Lobelia dortmanna*". This record was initially doubted by Macvicar (1896), but having published his rejection he refound the species at L. a'Mhill Aird the following year (Macvicar 1897c). It is apparently confined to a compact area NE of Arinagour (Fig. 4). It is most conspicuous when it grows in a band above water level or in shallow water at the edge of lochs, but it also occurs in water at least one metre deep; it is found over substrates of soft peat, fine gravel and mud. Plants grow clumped together in small patches or extensive mats, often with *Juncus bulbosus, Littorella uniflora, Lobelia dortmanna* and *Phragmites australis* and less frequently with a range of other aquatics characteristic of acidic waters. The sites were surveyed by RECF in 1978, LF & JMI in 1980 (Farrell 1983), CK & MARK on the BSBI meeting in 1989 and CDP & NFS in 1990. In 1989–1990 it was recorded in 15 lochs: L. a'Chrotha, L. Feisdlum and unnamed sites at 247591, 249595 and 245599 in 25 and L. Airigh Sitheachaidh, L. a'Mhill Aird, L. a'Mhill Aird Bhig, L. nam Badan, L. Ronard, L. na Cloiche and unnamed sites at 232605, 235602, 238613 and 242602 in 26. There is a record from one other site, SW of L. a'Mhill, 253598, where the species was seen by RECF in 1978 but not refound by NFS in a rather rapid visit in 1990. *E. aquaticum* is absent from lochs in the north-east uplands of Coll both north and south of this area. There have been suggestions that the species is spreading in Britain, but HH describes it as "excessively abundant in Loch a'Mhill Aird, and more or less plentiful in about a dozen lochs in the same area", which suggests that there has been little change in the last 50 years. A recent record from Tiree, from a lochan E of Moss, 969446, TD,

SPECIES LIST: VASCULAR PLANTS

1993, appears to be an error. Only vegetative *Baldellia ranunculoides*, which differs by not having transversely septate roots, was found at the site by LF in 1999.

Eriophorum angustifolium   Common Cottongrass   All

Common on wet moorlands and other boggy places throughout the islands.

Eriophorum vaginatum   Hare's-tail Cottongrass   (G); C 15,25,26

Not recorded from Tiree by Macvicar (1898) but described as "well distributed on Coll, Tiree and Gunna" by HH and as "frequent" on Tiree by Vose *et al.* (1957). There is one subsequent record for Tiree, from An Fhaodhail, which has not been confirmed and would be an unlikely habitat, and DAP could not find it anywhere on the island in 1990. We have therefore rejected the Tiree records as possible errors. For Coll, there are records from: Achamore, 15, BKC, 1998; bog pool W of L. a'Gharbh-airde, 210557, CDP, 1990; edge of L. na Cloiche, 2055, NFS, 1990; Ornsay, 2255, HH; moorland near Arnabost Farm, 25, JHH, 1947 (J. Heslop Harrison 1949); near Bousd, 26, BKC, KAHC & JWC, 1987.

Erodium cicutarium agg.   Stork's-bill   T all; (G); C 15,25,26

Well distributed on dunes, machair, and cultivated ground. There is one record of *E. cicutarium sens. str.* (Common Stork's-bill) from dunes W of Hynish, 976388, BHT, 1990, det. PMB, **GLAM**. *E. lebelii* (Sticky Stork's-bill) has been recorded from dunes S of Arnabost burn, 201603, JWC, 1987, det. HJN, **E**, and is possibly overlooked elsewhere.

Erophila verna sens. lat.   Whitlowgrass   T 94,04; C (15),16,26

Very rare on dunes with only five recent records: Traigh Bail'-a-mhuilinn, 94N, BSBI, 1990; An Fhaodhail, 04C, and Balephetrish, 04D, BSBI, 1990; machair NW of Cliad, 195602, JWC, 1992; Arnabost area, 208806, JWC, 1987.

Eryngium maritimum   Sea-holly   T 94,04; C 15,(26)

Very rare on foredunes. There are a number of records from Tiree, but the only recent localised sites are: Traigh Bail'-a-mhuilinn, 952406, many recorders up to CDP, 1997; Crossapol, 94, AMcGS, 1990; NE of Crossapol, 003437, CJC, 1995; Traigh Bhagh, 018439, CJC, 1995; Balephetrish Bay, 04, CWM, 1990. There is only one recent record from Coll: Bacan Seileach, 1151, JWC, 1987.

Escallonia macrantha   Escallonia   C 15

Self-seeding in high garden wall at Garden House, Uig, 15, JWC, 1990 and DAP & CDP, 1997.

Euphorbia cyparissias   Cypress Spurge   C 25

Garden plant, Arinagour, 223572, JWC, 1989, **E**.

Euphorbia helioscopia   Sun Spurge   T 93,94,04; C (25),26

A weed of arable and gardens, now only occasionally seen.

Euphorbia peplus   Petty Spurge   C 25

A garden weed: Achamore, 214596, DAP & CDP, 1997; Arinagour, 2257, AC, 1981 and DAP, CDP *et al.*, 1997.

Euphrasia   Eyebright

Eyebrights are often abundant in coastal turf over rock and sand, and on machair, and also occur in open turf in rocky moorland; they are recorded from all squares. We have been cautious in accepting records of this critical genus and have tended to accept only those records which have been confirmed by recent experts. Although some collections made on the BSBI meetings and subsequent visits have been critically determined, there is still scope for a detailed study of the genus on the islands. The fact that one Red Data Book species (*E. heslop-harrisonii*) and one nationally scarce species (*E. foulaensis*) have been discovered since 1987 suggests that such a study might prove very rewarding.

Euphrasia arctica subsp. *borealis*   T (04); C (25),(26)

The only confirmed records are: Odhrasgair, 04, SMM, 1897, det. Pugsley (1930) & PFY, **BM**; meadow beside L. Cliad, 25, C.W. Muirhead, 1951, det. EFW, **CLE** (Wallace 1953); Cornaigbeg, 26, UKD, 1967, det. PFY, **BM**. We have not accepted the records from the Salum-Urvaig area of Tiree (HH, as *E. brevipila*) and unlocalised but recent records from C 15 and C 25 in the absence of voucher specimens.

[*Euphrasia arctica* × *confusa*

This hybrid was recorded by HH from north-east Tiree, T 04, but requires confirmation, especially as the presence of *E. confusa* has not been confirmed recently.]

[*Euphrasia arctica* × *micrantha* or *nemorosa*

A specimen collected from shell sand, Crossapol Bay, 15, UKD, 1967, **BM**, was determined by PFY as '?*E. brevipila* × *micrantha* or *nemorosa* (eglandular)'.]

Euphrasia confusa C (25)

HH recorded this taxon from sites in T 94 and 04 and C 15, 25 and 26; he regarded it as common on Coll. There is a single specimen from Eilean Ornsay, 25, JWHH, 1940, det. PFY, **K**. Since then there have been no records although a specimen collected at 095473, the Balephetrish Bay area, by AB in 1990 was determined by AMcGS as a hybrid of *E. confusa*.

[*Euphrasia confusa* × *micrantha*

Recorded by HH from Sorisdale and Bousd, C 26.]

Euphrasia foulaensis T 05

Short *Festuca rubra* turf by sea, Urvaig, 0750, DAP & CDP, 1997, det. PFY, **CGE**. A single plant collected with *E. nemorosa*.

[*Euphrasia frigida*

E. frigida was tentatively reported from rocks near L. Cliad, C 25, by HH on the basis a plant "which Mr. Pugsley thinks possibly referable to this species" but there are no other records and the occurrence of this montane species at sea level on Coll is unlikely.]

Euphrasia heslop-harrisonii C 15,26

Upper saltmarsh on banks of drainage channels: E of Breachacha Castle, 163541, HJN, 1987, det. AJS, **E**, and SJL, 1989; An t-Inbhire, Cornaigbeg, 241632, SJL, 1989 (cf Leach in press).

Euphrasia micrantha T (94),04; G 15; C 15,25,26

Machair grassland, coastal turf, roadsides and the edge of marshes. This is the most frequently recorded species on Coll, whereas HH did not record it from Tiree and the later records are outnumbered by those of *E. nemorosa*. Expertly determined specimens are available from marsh near Heylipol church, Barrapol, 94, UKD, 1968, det. PFY, **BM**; short turf by sea opposite Eilean nan Gamhna, Gunna, 103511, CDP, 1989, det. PFY, **CGE**; Ballyhaugh, JWHH, 1940, det. PFY, **K**; machair E of Hogh Bay near Ballyhaugh, 15, UKD, 1967, det. PFY, **BM**; roadside from Arinagour to Gallanach, 25, C. W. Muirhead, 1951, det. EFW, **BM** (cf Muirhead 1952). Pugsley (1930) confirmed the identification of material collected on Tiree by C.E. Salmon. We have also accepted field records of this species.

Euphrasia nemorosa T 94,(04),05; C (15),(25),(26)

Frequent and often conspicuous on machair on Tiree but also found on coastal turf away from the machair. Expertly determined specimens (by PFY) are available from Hough, 94, VG, 1960, **LIV**; Heylipol church, Barrapol, 94, UKD, 1968, **BM**; Balephuil Bay, 942406 and SW of

Balephuil, 960405, CDP, 1997, **CGE**; Clachan Guest House, Baugh, 04, UKD, 1968, **BM**; Dun Mor a'Chaolais near Caoles, 04, UKD, 1968, **BM**; Urvaig, 0750, DAP & CDP, 1997, **CGE**; E of Hogh Bay near Ballyhaugh, 15, UKD, 1967, **BM**; Crossapol Bay, 15, C. W. Muirhead, 1951, **BM**; Grishipoll Bay, 15, C. W. Muirhead, 1951, **BM**; Arinagour, 224575, VG, 1960, **LIV**. PFY noted that the plants from Dun Mor a'Chaolais were "like S. English forms".

Euphrasia nemorosa hybrid   C (15)

One plant amongst a collection of *E. nemorosa* from machair E of Hogh Bay near Ballyhaugh, 15, UKD, 1967, **BM**, was determined by PFY as *E. nemorosa* × *?micrantha*.

[*Euphrasia ostenfeldii*

E. curta var. *glabrescens* was recorded by HH from Bousd, C 26, but the glabrous plants previously assigned to *E. curta* are now regarded as referable to other species or hybrids (Perring & Sell 1968).]

Euphrasia scottica   C (25),26

Moorland in central and north-east Coll; specimens doubtfully referable to this species have also been collected elsewhere. L. Cliad, 25, HH; moorland above L. a'Mhill Aird, 26, C. W. Muirhead, 1951, det. EFW (**BM, CLE**, cf Muirhead 1952, Wallace 1953); peaty pool edge, Eileraig, 261638, BSB, 1988. A specimen collected from the edge of saltmarsh, L. Eatharna, UKD, 1967, **BM**, was determined by PFY as probably referable to *E. scottica* "but corollas purple" and he also determined as ?*E. scottica* plants in a mixed collection of *E. nemorosa* and *E. micrantha* from marsh near Heylipol church, Barrapol, 94, UKD, 1968, **BM**.

[*Euphrasia tetraquetra*

Grishipoll Bay, C 15, C. W. Muirhead, 1951, det. EFW, **BM, CLE** (cf Muirhead 1952, Wallace 1953). Originally distributed under the synonym *E. occidentalis* var. *calvescens* but the only specimen at **BM** which has been seen by PFY was redetermined by him as *E. nemorosa*.]

*Fagus sylvatica   Beech   C 25

Planted at The Lodge, Arinagour, DAP, CDP *et al.*, 1997.

Fallopia convolvulus   Black-bindweed   T 94,04; (G); C (15),25,26

An uncommon weed of arable fields, with few recent records.

*Fallopia japonica × *sachalinensis (F.* × *bohemica)*   C 15

Cottage W of Garden House, Uig, 164542, DAP & CDP, 1997, det. JPB,

SPECIES LIST: VASCULAR PLANTS

CGE. *F. japonica* was recorded from the nearby Acha House, 1584, JWC, 1982, but the record may refer to this hybrid.

Festuca arundinacea   Tall Fescue   T (93),(94),04

Very rare, and only recorded very occasionally. The only detailed locality is from a roadside ditch, West Hynish, 93, JWC, 1982, **E**.

Festuca filiformis   Fine-leaved Sheep's-fescue   T (04); C (15)

Rarely recorded from dry moorland habitats. It may well be considerably more common. Balephetrish Hill, 014473, AMcGS, 1982, **E**; Ben Feall, 145547, JWC, 1984, det. AMcGS, **E**.

Festuca ovina agg.   Sheep's-fescue   T 93,94,04; (G); C all

Frequent and widespread in dry places, on machair and knolls on moorland.

Festuca pratensis   Meadow Fescue   T 93,94,04; C (25),(26)

Systematic surveys by CJC on Tiree revealed this species in 8 out of 33 leys sampled in 1975 and 5 out of 39 meadows sampled in 1987. Other observers have overlooked it, and there are only two other recent records.

Festuca rubra agg.   Red Fescue   All except C 16

The aggregate is very common and widespread on sandy pastures and dunes throughout. HH recorded various forms and varieties, but no work has been done since.

Festuca vivipara   Viviparous Sheep's-fescue   All except T 05; C 16

Fairly common on drier, rocky, moorland sites and more common on Coll than on Tiree.

Filipendula ulmaria   Meadowsweet   All except T 05

Widespread and common in wet places.

Fragaria vesca   Wild Strawberry   T (93); C 26

Very rare in scattered rocky places. Rocks, Hynish Head, 93, SMM (Macvicar 1898); cliff edge, Bousd, 26, HH; cave S of Sorisdale, 26, AW, 1989.

*Fraxinus excelsior   Ash   T (94); C (15),25

A very few records, presumably all of planted trees. Not recorded by HH.

*Fuchsia magellanica   Fuchsia   C (15),25,26

Self-sown on walls and persisting by the remnants of houses.

Fumaria

The genus has received little attention from botanists since HH, and the only recent records are for *F. bastardii*. More species may have been present in the past but we have preferred to treat records of other taxa as unconfirmed in the absence of voucher specimens. There is a record of an unidentified *Fumaria* for T 93, a square from which there are no species recorded: walled garden, Hynish, 9839, BSBI, 1990.

Fumaria bastardii   Tall Ramping-fumitory   T 94,04; (G); C 15,25,26

Described by HH as frequent in rye and oatfields in the Gott Bay, 04, area on Tiree, and in similar situations on the NW side of Coll. It, in common with other arable weeds, is now much less frequent. The only taxon we found in gardens and vegetable patches on Tiree and Coll in 1997 was *F. bastardii* var. *bastardii*.

[*Fumaria muralis* subsp. *boraei*   Common Ramping-fumitory

Arnabost, C 26, very rare, HH. Not recorded again. Extremely rare in NW Scotland, and rejected in the absence of a voucher specimen.]

[*Fumaria officinalis*   Common Fumitory

The only records are from T 04 and C 26. Both are unlocalised and undetermined records from the BSBI trips in 1967 and 1968, and are possibly errors for *F. bastardii*.]

[*Fumaria purpurea*   Purple Ramping-fumitory

Field N of Torastan, C 26, HH. Not recorded again. The only record for west Scotland is for Kintyre. Again, in the absence of a voucher specimen, the record is rejected.]

Galeopsis bifida   Bifid Hemp-nettle   T 94; C 15

First recorded in 1997. Arable fields SW of Balephuil, 960405, DAP & CDP, 1997; Garden House, Uig, 166542, DAP & CDP, 1997; SE of Uig, 1753, DAP & CDP, 1997.

Galeopsis speciosa   Large-flowered Hemp-nettle   T 94

Arable fields SW of Balephuil, 960405, DAP & CDP, 1997.

Galeopsis tetrahit sens. str.   Common Hemp-nettle   T 04; C 15,25,26

Arable and waste ground. Rare, with only one recent record from each 10km square.

Galium aparine   Cleavers   All

Widespread and very frequent on shingle, and as a weed in waste places.

Galium palustre   Common Marsh-bedstraw   All except C 16

Widespread and very frequent in wet places. A few records have been made of *G. palustre* subsp. *palustre*, from T 94,04 and C 26, and it is possibly the only subspecies present on the islands.

Galium saxatile   Heath Bedstraw   T 93,94,04; (G); C (15),25,26

Fairly widespread in moorland and rocky acid areas; absent from the machair and dunes. There are relatively few records from Tiree.

[**Galium uliginosum**   Fen Bedstraw

Recorded in similar places to *G. palustre* "but of much less frequent occurrence" by HH, but apart from one record from T 93, not recorded again. We have rejected these records as there are only a handful of records away from the mainland. Its presence in base-rich fens on Tiree is not impossible but the widespread distribution reported by HH suggests it was confused with *G. palustre*.]

Galium verum   Lady's Bedstraw   All

Plentiful and widespread, on machair, dunes and roadsides. Var. *maritimum* has been recorded from T 05 and C 15,25 and is undoubtedly much more widespread, being the common variant on the machair.

[**Gentianella amarella**   Autumn Gentian

N of L. Bhasapol, 962481, TD (Dargie 1993). Presumably an error for *G. campestris*.]

Gentianella campestris   Field Gentian   T 94,04,05; (G); C 15,16,(25),26

Quite widespread, but local and always in small numbers on dry rocky outcrops, or in sites with good drainage such as fixed dunes. On Tiree: Ceann a'Mhara, 94, DCL, 1973, and 934401, TD, 1993; near Scarinish, 04, SMM; An Dun, Balephetrish, 015481, TD, 1993; by L. Caol, 031456, IC, 1993; Vaul, 048486 and 048483, IC, 1993; Urvaig, 077504, DAP & CDP, 1997. Slightly more widespread on Coll.

Geranium dissectum   Cut-leaved Crane's-bill   T 94,04; C 15,25,26

An uncommon weed of fields and gardens, and waste ground.

Geranium molle   Dove's-foot Crane's-bill   All except G 05

Widespread, particularly on dunes and machair.

*__Geranium pratense__   Meadow Crane's-bill   T (04); C (15)

Recorded as a garden escape on Coll by HH and by cottage on road to Dun Mor, 04, DCL, 1973. Gardeners on Coll told HH that they had brought material from "wild stations along Loch Eatharna" but this supposed site has never been found by botanists.

[*Geranium pusillum*   Small-flowered Crane's-bill

Recorded "once in a field by the side of the Arnabost-Sorisdale road", C 26, HH. The only record from western Scotland.]

Geranium robertianum   Herb-Robert   T 04; C (15),26

The native status of this species is unclear. It has been recorded only once from Tiree, as a garden weed, Millton, DAP & CDP, 1997. But there are three records from Coll, all from rocky areas: Creag an Fhireoin, 15, HH; rock cleft above Clachard lochan, 26, JWC, 1987, **E**; rock fissures below Clachard, 26, JWC, 1987.

Geranium sanguineum   Bloody Crane's-bill   T 93,94,(04); G 15; C 15,16,26

Not uncommon on rock ledges on Ceann a'Mhara and Hynish in SW Tiree. There is a record from Caoles, 04, SH, 1984, but this may be only a garden escape as it has not been seen again. On Coll it is very abundant on the whole dune system at the west end of the island and rare on dunes north of Cliad and near Sorisdale.

*Glaucium flavum   Yellow Horned-poppy   C 25

A casual at Arinagour, 25, DAP, CDP *et al.*, 1997.

Glaux maritima   Sea-milkwort   All

Common and widespread in saltmarshes and on rocks exposed to spray.

Glyceria declinata   Small Sweet-grass   T (93),(94),04; C (25),(26)

Uncommon in poached pastures, but probably under-recorded. In fact it has only ever been recorded six times, with one recent record: Balephetrish, 04, BSBI, 1990. Murray (1980) suggests it is under-recorded on Skye.

Glyceria fluitans   Floating Sweet-grass   T 93,94,04; G 15; C 15,25,26

Common and widespread in wet places, especially ditches; most frequent on Tiree.

Gnaphalium uliginosum   Marsh Cudweed   T 93,(94),04; C 15,25,26

Rare and scattered in gateways and tracks, with three records from Tiree, and five from Coll.

*Gunnera manicata   Brazilian Giant-rhubarb   C (26)

Recorded by BSBI, 1967, from 26 but with no further details. A single plant of *Gunnera* sp. was later recorded by the stream W of Sorisdale Bay, 271632, CDP & NFS, 1989.

Gymnadenia conopsea   Fragrant Orchid   T (04); C (15),25,26

Only once recorded from Tiree, in small quantity with *Listera ovata* in damp turf near An Fhaodhail, 0144, CJC, 1983. On Coll it was described as "locally not rare" by HH but almost all recent records have all been from the NE of the island: near Arinagour, 25, BKC, 1987+; near Toraston, 26, HJN, 1987; L. a'Mhill Aird area, 26, JWC *et al.*, 1987; Sorisdale, 26, BSBI, 1989; Bousd, 253635, PFB, 1988. Subsp. *densiflora* has been recorded from Beg a'Mhonaidh, 15, JWC, 1984; Cornaigbeg meadows, 26, BSBI, 1967, BKC, 1984, **K**, and 243633, LF, 1999.

Hammarbya paludosa   Bog Orchid   T (04); C (25),26

Very rare and seldom recorded, in *Sphagnum* at the edges of lochans: near Balephetrish, 028477, BSBI, 1967; L. Cliad, 25, HH; near L. Ronard, 25, HH; L. a'Mhill Aird, 26, JWC *et al.*, 1987.

*****Hebe elliptica** × **speciosa (H.** × *franciscana)***   Hedge Veronica   T 94

One plant self-sown in crevice on wall, Balephuil, 968412, DAP & CDP, 1997.

Hedera helix   Common Ivy   C 15,25,26

Rarely found and seldom recorded, usually from cliffs and rocks. There is a garden record from Grishipoll, 15, HJN, 1987. Subsp. *helix* has been confirmed from C 25 and presumably all records are for this subspecies, as Coll lies beyond the northern limit of subsp. *hibernica*.

Helictotrichon pubescens   Downy Oat-grass   T 93,94,04; G 15; C 15,25,26

Not uncommon on cliff ledges and on grassy slopes by the sea. One of the dominants of the dry grassland of The Reef, recorded by CJC in 43 out of 50 4m^2 quadrats on the airfield in 1998.

Heracleum sphondylium   Hogweed   All

Common and widespread in ditches, on ledges and amongst rocks.

*****Hesperis matronalis***   Dame's-violet   T 94; C (15),25

An occasional outcast from gardens, only recorded recently from: The Sheiling, Kenovay, 995463, CDP & NFS, 1989; Burnside, Arinagour, 25, BKC, 1989.

Hieracium   Hawkweed

Hieracium species have been recorded recently only from C 15 and 26. The absence of *Hieracium* species from Tiree is remarkable, even considering the flat, grazed character of much of the island. There are small hawkweed populations on rock outcrops on Coll, and specimens have been collected from a range of these sites. The species recorded fall into four sections, *Cerinthoidea* (*H. ampliatum, H. iricum, H. shoolbredii*), *Oreadea* (*H. argenteum, H. caledonicum, H. subrude*), *Vulgata* (*H. orcadense, H. vulgatum*) and *Foliosa* (*H. subcrocatum*). All are widespread and many are common in western Scotland, the most local species being *H. subrude*. Nomenclature follows Kent (1992).

Hieracium ampliatum   C (26)

Calcareous rocks about half a mile north of Sorisdale, UKD, 1967, det. PDS & CW, **BM**.

Hieracium argenteum   C (15)

Ben Feall, Feall Bay, 1454, UKD, 1967, det. PDS & CW, **BM**.

Hieracium caledonicum   C 15,26

Rock outcrop S of L. Ballyhaugh, 175576, CDP & NFS, 1989, det. JB, **CGE**; rock outcrop near Arnabost, 2060, NFS, 1989, det. PDS, **CGE**.

Hieracium iricum   C 26

Shore, Cornaigbeg, 2363, JWC, 1991, det. DJMcC, **E**.

Hieracium orcadense   C (15)

Ben Feall, Feall Bay, 1454, UKD, 1967, det. PDS & CW, **BM**.

Hieracium shoolbredii   C 26

Recorded from several rock outcrops in NE Coll: rocks near sea near Sorisdale, 26, AMcGS, 1959, det. PDS & CW, **CGE**; rocks near Eileraig, 26, KAHC, 1985; slightly basic rock outcrop on W side of Allt an Inbhire, Cornaigbeg, 243638, CDP & NFS, 1989, det. JB, **CGE**; Traig Bhousd, 258637, CDP & NFS, 1989, det. JB, **CGE**.

Hieracium subcrocatum   C (25)

Recorded (as *H. strictum*) by HH from many cliff ledges between Arnabost Farm and L. Fada and confirmed (as *H. bartonii*) by Pugsley (1948).

Hieracium subrude   C (15)

Rocks, Totamore, 1756, KAHC, 1986, det. AMcGS, **E**.

Hieracium vulgatum (C)

Coll, R.B. Cooke, 1939, det. PDS & CW. No more details are known of this specimen, which was in **herb. R.B.C.** when seen by Sell & West and provides the basis for the record mapped in C 25 by Perring & Sell (1968).

[*Himantoglossum hircinum*   Lizard Orchid

Listed from Coll by MacCulloch (1819) as *Satyrium hircinum*, an obvious error.]

Hippuris vulgaris   Mare's-tail   T 94,04; C 15,25,26

Fairly common, especially on Tiree, at the shallow edge of lochans in places which dry out in summer. For a map of recent records, see Fig. 6.

Holcus lanatus   Yorkshire-fog   All except G 05

Widespread throughout the islands. It grows abundantly on islands and at the edge of some lochs enriched by bird droppings, with *Rumex acetosa*.

Holcus mollis   Creeping Soft-grass   T; C 15,25,26

HH gives Tiree with no locality, as does Dargie (1993). The few records for Coll are all from sheltered slopes under bracken and in gullies with trees: Soa, 1551, HJN, 1987; between L. Breachacha and L. Gortan, 15, DAP & CDP, 1997; W of Caolas-an-eilean, 25C, JWC, 1987 and DAP & CDP, 1997; Sorisdale, 26, BSBI, 1989.

Honckenya peploides   Sea Sandwort   All except T 05; C (25)

Common on sandy beaches on Tiree, less so on Coll, and occasional in saltmarshes.

Huperzia selago   Fir Clubmoss   T (94),04; C (15),(25),26

Not at all common on moorland outcrops. Recent records: NW of Kirkapol, 04, BSBI, 1990; Bousd area, 26L, JWC, BKC & KAHC, 1987.

Hyacinthoides non-scripta   Bluebell, Wild Hyacinth

T 93,04,04; C 15,25,26

On Tiree only frequent on rock ledges on Ceann a'Mhara and Ben Hynish. On Coll rather more widespread on rocks and amongst bracken, especially in the east of the island.

Hydrocotyle vulgaris   Marsh Pennywort   All

Widespread and common in wet pastures, short goose-grazed turf, ditches and by the edge of lochans.

Hymenophyllum wilsonii   Wilson's Filmy-fern   C (15),26

Very rare in sheltered places on cliffs: Grishipoll, 15, BSBI, 1967, **BM**; Druim Nan Carn, 268640, BSB, 1988.

Hypericum androsaemum   Tutsan   C 15,25,26

Rare and apparently native in a few places, often amongst rocks. The recent records are Allt Mor, Uig, 1654, DAP & CDP, 1997; E of Cliad Farm, 207594, MEB & PFB, 1990; A'Chroic, 227629, JWC, 1988; Eileraig, 260639, PFB, 1988.

Hypericum elodes   Marsh St John's-wort   T 93,94,04; G 05; C (15),25,26

Fairly frequent in lochans, pools and streams on Tiree; much less common on Coll other than in the far north-east.

Hypericum pulchrum   Slender St John's-wort   T 93,(94),04; (G); C 15,25,26

Relatively common in heathy places, particularly on Coll.

Hypericum tetrapterum   Square-stalked St John's-wort
                                  T (93),(94),04; G 05; C 15,(25),26

Relatively uncommon in marshes. There is only one recent record on Tiree: An Cnap area, 04P, DAP & CDP, 1997. On Coll it has been found E of Ben Feall, 1554, CG & AGP, 1999, and at several localities in 26.

Hypochaeris radicata   Cat's-ear   All except T 05

Frequent and widespread in many habitats, including dunes, rock out-crops and waste places. Subsp. *ericetorum* has been collected from a coastal rock S of Caoles, 125525, CDP & NFS, 1989, det. PDS, **CGE**, and is probably more widespread.

*****Inula helenium***   Elecampane   T 94,(04)

A long-established alien, first found by EB at Balephetrish, 04 (Macvicar 1898) and described by HH as "here and there on Tiree; especially common near Middleton". Subsequent records are all from W Tiree, and include the following from road verges: Barrapol, 94, DAP & CDP, 1997; E of Balevullin, 9647, DAP, 1997; near Balemartine, 9741, CDP & NFS, 1990; Druimbuidhe, 9745, CDP & NFS, 1989.

Iris pseudacorus   Yellow Flag   All

Extremely common especially in pastures on Tiree that have 'gone back' with *Juncus* species, but frequent in many wet habitats. It fringes streams flowing over sand but is not usually present as an emergent at the edge of lochs.

Isoetes echinospora   Spring Quillwort   T (94),04; C 15,25,26

Rare in lochs on Tiree: L. an Eilein, 983437, AAS, 1982, **BM**; L. Cnoc Ibrig, 0245, CDP & SDW, 1990, **CGE**; L. Dubh a'Gharraidh Fail, 026485, CDP & NFS, 1989; L. Dubh, 031485, CK, MARK & CDP, 1990, **CGE**. More common on Coll, where it was first recorded at L. Airigh Meall Bhreide, 25, by C.W. Muirhead in 1951. There are recent records from 12 lochs, where it grows over a range of substrates from fine silt to stones and rocks. For a map of recent records, see Fig. 5.

Isoetes lacustris   Quillwort   C 15,25

Much less common on Coll than *I. echinospora* with confirmed records only from gravelly or rocky sites in four lochs: L. nan Cinneachan, 1856, CDP & NFS, 1990; L. Ronard, 2055, NFS, 1990; L. Boidheach, 201566, NFS, 1990; L. nan Geadh, 2358, CDP, 1990; all **CGE**. At L. Ronard *I. echinospora* and *I. lacustris* grow together. We have rejected HH's records of *I. lacustris* as he failed to record the commoner *I. echinospora*.

Isolepis cernua   Slender Club-rush   C (15)

Recorded as "not rare in damp places near Cliad and other points in the west of Coll", HH, but never recorded again. However, it is found in coastal habitats in the west of Mull, on Islay and the south of the Outer Hebrides. It is easily overlooked as *I. setacea*.

Isolepis setacea   Bristle Club-rush   All except G 15, C 16

Quite widespread in bare damp peaty places, often those trampled by livestock, but never very common.

Juncus acutiflorus   Sharp-flowered Rush   All except T 05

Widespread and fairly frequent in all wet places.

Juncus ambiguus   Frog Rush   T 04,05; C 15,25

Rare, but almost certainly overlooked, in saltmarshes and damp sand by the sea: Traigh Mhor, 043469, CDP & NFS, 1989, **CGE**; Lon Fhadamuill, 073493, DAP, CDP & NFS, 1990; Urvaig, 076502, DAP & CDP, 1997; Crossapol, 129529, CDP & NFS, 1989; Arinagour, 224571, CDP & NFS, 1989, **CGE**.

Juncus articulatus   Jointed Rush   All

Widespread and fairly frequent in wet places.

Juncus balticus   Baltic Rush   T 94,04

Rare and restricted. The largest stands are on The Reef where there are extensive patches on damp machair, but it also occurs in a few areas of sandy soils by lochans: N shore of L. Bhasapol, 969475, MH, 1990; marshy ground NW of L. a'Phuill, 949425, DAP, 1990; S side of L. a'Phuill, 9541, AMcGS, 1990; L. an Eilein, 9843, BSBI, 1990; An Fhaodhail and adjacent areas, 0043, 0143, 0144, 0145, many recorders up to BSBI, 1990, TD, 1993, and CJC, 1995; L. Riaghain, 035469, AMcGS, 1990.

Juncus bufonius　　　　Toad Rush　　　　All except C 16

Widespread in wet sandy places, and on tracks.

Juncus bulbosus　　　　Bulbous Rush　　　　All

Frequent in all wet habitats including lakes (as the aquatic variant).

Juncus conglomeratus　　　　Compact Rush　　　　All except T 05

Widespread in wet places, but not particularly well recorded.

Juncus effusus　　　　Soft-rush　　　　All

Widespread and very common throughout. In 1997 DAP, CDP *et al.* recorded var. *effusus* twice, in C 15,25 (but it is presumably more widespread), var. *spiralis* six times, in T 04,05 and C 15,25 and var. *subglomeratus* twice, in C 15,25.

Juncus gerardii　　　　Saltmarsh Rush　　　　All

Frequent in saltmarshes, and amongst rocks in the spray zone.

Juncus maritimus　　　　Sea Rush　　　　C (25),26

Very rare in saltmarshes: L. Eatharna, 2257, HH and BSBI, 1967, but not seen since; Cornaigbeg, 241632, SJL, 1989.

Juncus squarrosus　　　　Heath Rush　　　　T 93,94,04; C (15),25,26

Common on heathy ground only, and thus only scattered on Tiree, but supposedly more frequent in the east of Coll. However, it is very poorly recorded.

Juniperus communis　　　　Common Juniper　　　　C 15,25,26

Quite widespread in heathy and rocky habitats on Coll, including crannogs, but populations usually consist of only a few plants. There is only one recent record for W Coll: one large plant on coast between L. Breachacha and L. Gortan, 169527, DAP & CDP, 1997, but it is more frequent in the east. All recent records belong to *J. communis* subsp. *nana* but HH did record subsp. *communis* from the Druim Fishaig ridges, 26.

Koeleria macrantha   Crested Hair-grass   All

Abundant in machair throughout.

Lamium amplexicaule   Henbit Dead-nettle   T (04); C (25),26

A rare weed, only recorded three times in ruderal habitats, and recently only at a dump, Arnabost, 204600, JWC, 1987.

Lamium confertum   Northern Dead-nettle   T 93,94,04; C (25),26

An arable weed, with scattered records only. Abundant in walled garden, Hynish, 9839, BSBI, 1990. Not seen in 1997 on either island.

Lamium hybridum   Cut-leaved Dead-nettle   T all; C 15,25,26

Scattered in arable, waste ground and gardens.

Lamium purpureum   Red Dead-nettle   T 93,94,04; C 15,25,26

More of a garden weed than *L. hybridum*, but fairly frequent where it occurs.

*****Lapsana communis***   Nipplewort   T (04); C (15),25

A very rare casual, only recorded recently at Achamore, 25, AW, 1988.

*****Larix decidua* × *kaempferi (L. × marschlinsii)***   Hybrid Larch   C 26

With *Populus tremula* and *Sorbus aucuparia* in gulley on S side of L. Fada, 255619, JWC, KAHC & BKC, 1987 and CDP, 1989.

*****Larix kaempferi***   Japanese Larch   C 15

Only recorded by BSB, 1988.

Lathyrus linifolius   Bitter-vetch   T (04); C 15,25,26

Amongst rocks, in heathy ground. Only once recorded on Tiree, 04, AMcGS, 1959, no locality. On Coll known from: between L. Breachacha and L. Gortan, 15R, DAP & CDP, 1997; E of Arnabost, 219597, BSB, 1988; near Sorisdale, 274634, JWC, 1988.

Lathyrus pratensis   Meadow Vetchling   All

Common in ditches and on roadsides throughout the islands.

Lemna minor   Common Duckweed   All except T 93, C 16

Occasional in streams, ditches and pools near the coast, or on waterside mud, but certainly not common. Usually present in small quantity (only one frond seen at some sites!) but abundant at the small dam on Balephetrish Hill, 015473, CDP & NFS, 1989 and 1990. For a map of recent records, see Fig. 9.

Leontodon autumnalis Autumn Hawkbit All

Plentiful on machair, in fields and on the upper edges of saltmarshes, where it is a small glabrous plant, var. *salina.*

[*Leontodon hispidus* Rough Hawkbit

Recorded only from An Fhaodhail, 0144, BSBI, 1990; Crossapol to Ben Feall, 15, HH. Almost certainly errors for *L. saxatilis,* and similarly omitted from the Floras of Mull and Skye.]

Leontodon saxatilis Lesser Hawkbit T (94),04; C 15,25,26

Rarely recorded from dunes. In several sites at the western end of Coll, 15, but elsewhere only recorded recently from An Fhaodhail, 04C, BSBI, 1990; N of Cliad, 2059, DAP, CDP *et al.,* 1997; W of Arnabost, 2060, JWC, 1987.

Leucanthemum vulgare Oxeye Daisy T (94),04; C all

Rare and scattered on rocky outcrops, sand dunes and as a weed in arable fields.

Leymus arenarius Lyme-grass T 94,04

Very rare on sandy shores: Balemartine, 986411, TD, 1993; mouth of An Fhaodhail, 016439, TD, 1993; shore by L. Aulaig, 04, JWC, 1982.

Ligusticum scoticum Scots Lovage T 93,94,04; G 05; C 15,25,(26)

Confined to gullies and ledges on sea cliffs. Quite common on Ceann a'Mhara and Ben Hynish in W Tiree, and between Balephetrish and Vaul Bay. Described by HH as "on sea cliffs along the north west shore of Coll, not at all rare", there are only scattered recent records. It would be surprising if it was not still there.

*Ligustrum vulgare Wild Privet T 04; C (25)

The only records are: Am Beannan Ruadh, 035491, BSBI, 1990; Arinagour, 25, JWC, 1984. Presumably planted.

Linum catharticum Fairy Flax All

Widespread and frequent on machair and pastures and on roadsides.

Listera cordata Lesser Twayblade C (26)

Under heather and bracken, L. a'Mhill Aird, 26, HH. The only record. There are other scattered records along the west coast of Scotland.

Listera ovata   Common Twayblade   T (94),04; C 15,26

Very rarely recorded from damp ground on the machair. The only recent records are: The Reef, 0144, AMcGS & BHT, 1990, and CJC, 1995; Machair Mhor, 15, JWC, 1998; Cornaigbeg, 234629, JWC, 1987.

Littorella uniflora   Shoreweed   T 94,04; C all

In shallow water in virtually every burn, loch and lochan, especially in sites where water levels fluctuate, including pools that dry out in summer. For a map of recent records, see Fig. 7.

Lobelia dortmanna   Water Lobelia   T 94,04; C 15,25,26

Frequent in all the more acidic lochs, especially where the substrate is stony although it also grows over sand, soft silt and peat. For a map of recent records, see Fig. 8.

*Lolium multiflorum   Italian Rye-grass
                                                       T (93),94,(04); C (15),(25),26

Well recorded as a relict of cultivation by HH, but very uncommonly since. In fact the only recent records are: Crossapol, 9944, DAP & CDP, 1997; Dun Morbhaidh, 236631, JWC, 1988.

Lolium perenne   Perennial Rye-grass   All

A common constituent of improved pastures, but also found in machair and other sandy areas.

Lonicera periclymenum   Honeysuckle   T 93,(94),(04); C 15,25,26

Sparsely distributed in rocky places, including crannogs. On Tiree only recently recorded from Ben Hynish, 93, BSBI, 1990 (it is odd there is no Ceann a'Mhara record since 1967). More frequent in gullies on Coll.

Lotus corniculatus   Common Bird's-foot-trefoil   All

Very frequent in most habitats, particularly on the machair.

Lotus pedunculatus   Greater Bird's-foot-trefoil   T (94),(04); C 15,25

Very uncommon in ditches. Only known on Tiree from An Fhaodhail, 04, PW, 1983, with a further unlocalised record from W Tiree, 94, VG, 1960. IC recorded it at three sites around Gott and Salum (Dargie 1993) but quadrat details from her survey suggest an error for *L. corniculatus*. On Coll it has long been known from The Lodge, Arinagour, 25, but was found in some quantity in three places in the Uig area, 15, by DAP & CDP, 1997.

Luzula campestris   Field Wood-rush   T 93,94,04,(05); (G); C 15,25,26

Frequent in grassy places throughout.

Luzula multiflora   Heath Wood-rush   All except T 05

Frequent in moist places on moors and grassland. Subsp. *congesta* seems widely distributed, but has only been recorded separately in C 15 and 25. Subsp. *multiflora* too is only recorded for C 15. More work needs to be done.

Luzula pilosa   Hairy Wood-rush   T 04; C (15),25,26

On rock ledges and in sheltered places in gullies, rare. Only recorded once on Tiree, cliffs below Vaul, 0448, DAP & CDP, 1997. Uncommon on Coll, with localised records from near Caolas-an-eilean, 2155, DAP & CDP, 1997 and near Sorisdale, 268635, BSBI, 1989.

Luzula sylvatica   Great Wood-rush   C 15,25,26

In similar localities to the last, but more frequent.

Lychnis flos-cuculi   Ragged-Robin   All

Frequent and widespread in all damp areas.

*****Lycium barbarum***   Duke of Argyll's Teaplant   T (04)

Recorded once from the Balephetrish area, BSBI, 1968.

Lycopus europaeus   Gypsywort   (G); C 25

Recorded by HH from wet places by the sea on Gunna, and adjoining Eilean Ornsay, 2255. Refound by Caolas-an-eilean, 223558, DAP & CDP, 1997, and also recorded at Bagh Feisdlum, 249587, PT, 1989, and inland by stream on N side of L. Airigh Leirge, 237582, CDP, 1990.

Lysimachia nemorum   Yellow Pimpernel   C 15,25,26

Scattered, but very rare, on rocky ledges and by ditches: between L. Breachacha and L. Gortan, 15R, DAP & CDP, 1997; ditch at Arinagour, 25, JMcK, 1989; several places around Sorisdale, 26.

*****Lysimachia nummularia***   Creeping-Jenny   T 04

Well established by SE corner of L. an Eilein, several recorders from HH up to BSBI, 1990. Probably an escape here from Island House, as there are no other records for the Western Isles.

Lythrum portula   Water-purslane   T 94,04; C 15,25,26

Occasional in swamps, small pools, poached ground near water or depressions on rutted tracks.

Lythrum salicaria   Purple-loosestrife   T (94),(04); C 15,25,26

Very local in damp fields and marshes. No recent records from Tiree, and only six from Coll.

*Malva sylvestris   Common Mallow   T 94,04,05

Tracksides and waste ground near buildings, first seen in 1990. Ceann a'Mhara, 9340, AW, 1990; Balephetrish Farm, 013473, CDP & NFS, 1990; Urvaig House, 080501, DAP & CDP, 1997.

*Matricaria discoidea   Pineappleweed   All except G 05, C 16

Recorded by HH as near houses in several places on Coll and found on Tiree in 1952 by KNGM (Wallace 1954). It is now widespread on tracks and in gateways throughout the islands.

Medicago lupulina   Black Medick   T (94),04,05; C (15),(25),(26)

Only twice recorded in recent years: Scarinish, 043448, DAP, 1997; Urvaig, 05, AW, 1990. It is difficult to believe that it has disappeared from the other sites but the species is certainly rare on the islands. However, Macvicar (1898) described it as "locally very common".

Melampyrum pratense   Common Cow-wheat   C 15,25,26

Rare on heathy ledges, under bracken, and in *Sphagnum* bogs. In C 15 only recorded from above L. Gortan, 15R, various recorders up to DAP & CDP, 1997, but scattered in E Coll.

Mentha aquatica   Water Mint   All

Widely distributed in wet places throughout.

*Mentha aquatica × *spicata (M.* × *piperita)*   Peppermint   T (94)

Wet ground W of L. Bhasapol, HH.

*Mentha spicata   Spear Mint   C (25)

Recorded by HH from Cliad. Probably a short-lived garden throwout.

*Mentha spicata × *suaveolens (M.* × *villosa)*   Apple-mint   T (94)

Balemartine village green, BSBI, 1968, det. RMH, **BM**.

*Mentha suaveolens   Round-leaved Mint   C 25,26

Known to HH at Arinagour. There are two recent records: Arinagour, 224572, DAP, CDP *et al.*, 1997 (the cultivar 'Variegata'); dump, Sorisdale, 26, JWC, 1988.

Menyanthes trifoliata   Bogbean   T 93,94,04; C 15,25,26

Abundant, especially in peaty habitats such as the sheltered bays of acidic lochs, *Sphagnum* bogs and old peat cuttings. Also present in pools at the back of dunes. For a map of recent records, see Fig. 8.

Mertensia maritima   Oysterplant   T 94,(04),05; (G)

Rare high up on beaches of shingle and coarse sand, apparently usually persisting for only a few years at any one site. Aird Mor Bay, 994476, BR, 1988, CDP & NFS, 1989 and LF, 1999, a healthy colony with 90 flowering plants and 10 vegetative rosettes in 1989, and 186 adults, 15 juveniles and 12 seedlings in 1999; Salum Bay, 04, 1896 or 1897, EB (Macvicar 1898); 1 plant NW of Urvaig, 077502, DAP & CDP, 1997; "in one or two little bays on the north shore of Gunna", HH.

*Mimulus cupreus × ***guttatus (M.*** × ***burnetii)***   Coppery Monkeyflower C 15

"Both sides of the burn running into Grishipoll Bay, a lovely sight", BSBI, 1967, **BM**, BKC, 1983, **E**, and JWC, 1988 and 1997.

Molinia caerulea   Purple Moor-grass   All

Common, especially on moorland and around lochans; more frequent on Coll than Tiree. The dead leaves often blow into peaty waters, persisting as a mat which appears to suppress the growth of aquatic plants.

Montia fontana   Blinks   All except G 15, C 16

Scattered, and only fairly common in wet places.

Myosotis arvensis   Field Forget-me-not   T 93,94,04; C all

Fairly common in cultivated soils.

Myosotis discolor   Changing Forget-me-not   T (93),94,04; C 15,25,26

Described by HH as "plentiful in dry places", there are only two recent records for Tiree: Barrapol, 9542, BSBI, 1990; An Traigh-lochain, 0849, BSBI, 1990. Similarly on Coll it has been found W of Breachacha Castle, 15, DAP, CDP *et al.*, 1997; Cliad Farm, 2059, JWC, 1998; S of Gallanach, 2160, JWC, 1988.

Myosotis laxa   Tufted Forget-me-not   All

The most frequent of the water forget-me-nots, widespread in marshy places.

Myosotis scorpioides   Water Forget-me-not   T 94,04; C 15,(26)

Rare in wet places. The only recent records are: L. an Eilein, 9843, BSBI, 1990; An Fhaodhail, 015453, CDP, 1990; Lochan a'Chuirn, 119523, DAP & CDP, 1997.

Myosotis secunda   Creeping Forget-me-not   All except T 05, C 16

Quite uncommon in wet places, although locally frequent by An Fhaodhail.

Myrica gale   Bog-myrtle   T 94,04; (G); C 15,25,26

Not uncommon in boggy places on Tiree, with about seven sites in total. Much more frequent in central and east Coll.

Myriophyllum alterniflorum   Alternate Water-milfoil   T 94,04; C all

Frequent in lochans, and more common and widespread than *M. spicatum*. Prostrate, worm-like plants which grow with *Chara aspera* over sand in the exposed northern shore of L. an Eilein appear to be referable to var. *americanum*. For a map of recent records, see Fig. 8.

Myriophyllum spicatum   Spiked Water-milfoil   T 94,04; (G); C 15,25,(26)

In larger lochs and small rock pools near the coast. Quite common in W Tiree, only seen recently on Eilean Frachlan on Gunna and very rare on Coll away from the western end, with only one recent record: L. Cliad, 206589, CDP & NFS, 1989.

*****Myrrhis odorata***   Sweet Cicely   T 04; C 15,26

A garden escape, with recent records from: 04J, BSBI, 1990; Uig, 15, JWC, 1998; Sorisdale, 270632, JWC, 1988.

Najas flexilis   Slender Naiad   C 15,26

Discovered on Coll as recently as 1987, this aquatic of clear water is most frequent in Britain in western Scotland. L. Ballyhaugh, 176582, HJN, 1987, **E**, and CDP & NFS, 1989, **CGE**; L an t-Sagairt, 251609, CDP & NFS, 1989. In L. Ballyhaugh it was frequent throughout most of the lake in 1989 (when water levels were low), growing as small plants in water 40–50 cm deep with *Potamogeton rutilus* and *Chara aspera*.

Nardus stricta   Mat-grass   All

Widespread and frequent on moors and cliffs.

Narthecium ossifragum   Bog Asphodel   All except G 15

Common and widespread in all boggy places.

Nymphaea alba   White Water-lily   C 15,25,26

Frequent and sometimes abundant in lochs in the centre and east of Coll. Not found in the west, and only recorded in 15 at L. Fada, 1958, CDP, 1990. All records are for the species, although HH did differentiate subsp. *occidentalis* from NE of Arinagour. For a map of recent records, see Fig. 4.

Odontites vernus   Red Bartsia   All

Not uncommon and widespread in fields and waste ground. Subsp. *serotinus* has been confirmed from dune turf at Balephuil Bay, 945407, CDP, 1997, det. PDS, **CGE**, and is probably much more widespread. Subsp. *pumilus* is a distinctive, dwarf unbranched plant which occurs locally by the coast, being recorded on Tiree from dune turf W of Abhainn a'Bheidhe, 955412, and waste ground near the river N of Scarinish, 048454 (both CDP & NFS, 1989, det. PDS, **CGE**) and on Coll from moist dune turf N of Cliad, 203599, DAP, CDP *et al.*, 1997, det. PDS, **CGE**. This is the plant which Stace (1997) calls subsp. *litoralis*, but PDS tells us that this name is misapplied to the British plant.

Oenanthe crocata   Hemlock Water-dropwort
                              T 93,94,04; G 15; C (15),25,26

Fairly widespread in ditches and similar habitats, but with only nine recent records. Still present at one of the two sites recorded by HH, the sea shore opposite Eilean Ornsay, 2255, DAP, CDP *et al.*, 1997.

Oenanthe lachenalii   Parsley Water-dropwort
                              T 94,04,05; G 05,15; C 15,26

Quite common on Tiree in marshy places and in saltmarshes. Much rarer on Coll, with only two records away from the west of the island. Dwarf plants occur on Tiree in turf at the edge of L. a'Phuill and L. Bhasapol and amongst coastal plants at Urvaig.

Ononis repens   Common Restharrow   T 04

Recorded by HH from near Acairseid an Duin, Millton, 04. The only recent record is from Salum Bay, 066487, BSBI, 1990, where it was still present by a track in the dunes, DAP & CDP, 1997. The species is extremely uncommon in the Western Isles. There is a specimen of *O. spinosa* from Mull in **E**, but our plant is definitely *O. repens*.

Ophioglossum azoricum   Small Adder's-tongue   T 94,04

Locally frequent in short turf of grazed machair grassland in two sites at Kenovay, 998454 and 002455, CJC, 1995, and in ungrazed grassland within the airport fence, at 002455, CJC, 1995. *O. vulgatum sens. strict.* was recorded in the same survey from damp slacks on The Reef. *O. azoricum* is recorded from many sites along the west coast of Scotland. No voucher specimens were collected.

Ophioglossum vulgatum   Adder's-tongue   T 94,04; (G); C 15,(25),26

In dune slacks, in meadows and under bracken. Rare, with 13 recent records (seven from Tiree, six from Coll). Recorded by CJC in 8 out of 50 1m^2 quadrats on dry machair at Tiree airfield, CJC, 1998.

Orchis mascula   Early-purple Orchid   T (94),(04); G 05; C 15,25,26

Rare on rock ledges and similar places: recorded up to 1984 from Ceann a'Mhara and Beinn Hough on Tiree. There are recent records from the other islands: Gunna, 05, BSBI, 1987; W of Breachacha Castle, 152538, CG & AGP, 1999; behind Totronald House, 1656, BKC, 1987+; Arinagour, 2256, LF, 1997; Dun Morbhaidh area, 234635, JWC, 1987.

Oreopteris limbosperma   Lemon-scented Fern   C 15,25,26

Rarely recorded from sheltered gullies but possibly more frequent than these records suggest: Allt Mor, 1654, DAP & CDP, 1997; S end of L. Cliad, 210582, BSB, 1988; near Cranaig, 212603, JWC, 1988. We have not accepted the one unsubstantiated record from Tiree: Carnan Mor, 94, BSBI, 1968.

Osmunda regalis   Royal Fern   C 15,25,26

Not uncommon in north and east Coll, in mires, along streams and loch edges, and on ungrazed islands in lochs. Rare in W Coll, only at Allt Mor, 160547, JWC, 1984 and DAP & CDP, 1997.

Oxalis acetosella   Wood-sorrel   C (15),25,26

"At first sight seemingly rare; actually quite common on rock ledges and amongst bracken at the base of cliffs" HH. Very sparingly recorded since, but doubtless under-recorded for the reasons implied by HH.

*****Oxalis corniculata***   Procumbent Yellow-sorrel   T 04

Garden weed at Millton, 087476, DAP & CDP, 1997.

*****Papaver argemone***   Prickly Poppy   (C)

Recorded for Coll by Macvicar (1897a).

Papaver dubium subsp. ***dubium***   Long-headed Poppy

T 93,94,04; C (15),(25),26

Only occasional in arable fields and gardens.

__Papaver hybridum__   Rough Poppy   T (04)

In a potato patch at Baugh, BSBI, 1968, **BM**.

__Papaver rhoeas__   Common Poppy   T (04)

Recorded by Macvicar (1898) for Tiree as "only one plant seen in 1897 in a ryegrass field belonging to the Hotel". Reported from N of Ruaig, 065480, IC (Dargie 1993) but perhaps as an error for *P. dubium.*

__*Parnassia palustris*__   Grass-of-Parnassus   T (94),04; C all

In dune slacks and ditches, and even in *Sphagnum* on moorland, but seemingly rare. The only recent records for Tiree are from An Fhaodhail, 0144, BSBI, 1990, and 0045, 0144, 0146, CJC, 1995. Although there are recent records for Coll, most of these are in the NE of the island. By contrast, HH recorded it as "not at all rare behind the dunes on Coll".

__*Pedicularis palustris*__   Marsh Lousewort   All except T 05

Widespread in wet ground, especially in moorlands, and in pools on machair.

__*Pedicularis sylvatica*__   Lousewort   All except T 05

Seemingly as common as *P. palustris,* in similar habitats.

__*Persicaria amphibia*__ Amphibious Bistort T (93),94,04; (G); C 15,25,26

Seemingly uncommon as a floating aquatic other than in W Tiree but scattered in wet fields throughout.

[__*Persicaria bistorta*__   Bistort

Recorded from N of Tiree Aerodrome, 002461, TD (Dargie 1993) but we assume that this is an error.]

__*Persicaria hydropiper*__   Water-pepper   T 94,04; C (26)

Recorded from nine sites on Tiree by TD in 1993. These are the only recent records. Perhaps it is more obvious later in the year when he was recording, so we have accepted the records albeit with slight misgivings. Only ever recorded on Coll by HH as "not uncommon along streams from Gallanach to Cornaigmore". As it is fairly widespread on Mull, and seemingly so on Ardnamurchan, it is difficult to say categorically that this is an error.

[__*Persicaria hydropiper* × *maculosa (P.* × *intercedens)*__

Recorded only by HH, from A'Chroic, 26, but Stace *et al.* (1975) say that hybrids have been over-recorded in this genus.]

Persicaria maculosa   Redshank   T 93,94,04; G 15; C 15,25,26

Fairly commonly recorded, but almost always as an arable weed, and in gardens. Most of the recent records are from NE Coll.

[*Persicaria vivipara*   Alpine Bistort

Listed by MacCulloch (1819) as an aquatic growing with *Iris pseudacorus* on Tiree, an obvious slip for *P. amphibia*.]

*Petasites hybridus   Butterbur   T (93),94; C (15),26

Well established on streamsides, roadsides and waste ground: recorded recently at Traigh Bail'-a-mhuillinn, 955474, AMcGS, 1990; S of Cornaigmore, 9946, DAP & CDP, 1997; dump near Arnabost, 26, JWC, 1987.

*Petroselinum crispum   Garden Parsley   C 26

Recorded once from a dump at Cliad, JWC, 1987.

Phalaris arundinacea   Reed Canary-grass   T 93,94,04; C all

Infrequently recorded from streamsides, usually not far from the sea. Perhaps most common in the An Fhaodhail area on Tiree.

Phegopteris connectilis   Beech Fern   C (25),(26)

HH recorded this only in a ravine near Eilean nam Faoileag, 2559. The only other record is from L. a'Mhill Aird, 26, BSBI, 1967 (Duncan 1968b). The species is frequent in western Scotland

*Phleum pratense sens. lat.   Timothy   T 93,94,04; C (15),25,26

P. pratense is rarely recorded. *P. pratense sens. strict.* is widely sown in leys and was recorded in 22 of 39 fields sampled by CJC in 1987. It is probably overlooked by many recorders. *P. bertolonii* (Smaller Cat's-tail) has been recorded only by the BSBI trip in 1967 and subsequently at An Fhaodhail, 016441, TD, 1993; Balephetrish, 011466, TD, 1993; Arinagour, 225562, DAP, 1997.

Phragmites australis   Common Reed   T 93,94,04; G 15; C all

Common in lochans and other marshy places, and particularly frequent in N and E Coll. For a map of recent records, see Fig. 5.

Phyllitis scolopendrium   Hart's-tongue   T (94),(04); C (15),26

A rare fern of rock crevices. HH gives three localities on Coll and one on Tiree. The 1967 and 1968 BSBI trips recorded it from four 10km squares. Since then it has only been recorded once, from Eileraig, 260639, KAHC, 1988.

*__*Picea abies*__   Norway Spruce   C 25
Planted at Arinagour, 25, DAP, CDP *et al.*, 1997.

*__*Picea sitchensis*__   Sitka Spruce   C 25,26
Planted at Arinagour, 25, BSB, 1988; a young tree cast up on shore planted on hillside at Sorisdale and growing well, 26, JWC, 1988.

*__*Pilosella aurantiaca* subsp. *carpathicola*__   Fox-and-cubs   C 25
Only recorded at Arinagour, 25, where it was collected from a wall by C. W. Muirhead, 1951, det. PDS & CW, **CLE**, and recorded as naturalised in the garden of Craigdarroch, 25, by KAHC, 1983, and with *Erinus alpinus* on the perimeter wall of the same garden, 223572, CDP & NFS, 1989. The attribution to subsp. *carpathicola* is based on the 1951 specimen alone.

Pilosella officinarum   Mouse-ear-hawkweed
T 93,94,04; G 15; C 15,25,26

Frequent in dry grassland or short heath, especially where the turf is broken by rocks. The following subspecies have been recorded, following the taxonomy and nomenclature of Sell (1998):

Subsp. *euronota*: near Caoles, 124525, JWC, 1986, det. AMcGS, **E**.

Subsp. *melanops*: Balephetrish Hill, 016473, CDP & NFS, 1989, det. PDS, **CGE**; E of Ben Feall, 150546, CDP & NFS, 1989, det. PDS, **CGE**.

Subsp. *micradenia*: W of Arnabost, 208608, JWC, 1987, det. AMcGS, **E**.

Subsp. *officinarum*: N of Cliad, 1960, JWC, 1991.

Subsp. *tricholepia*: near Vaul, 0448, AMcGS, 1990; opposite Eilean nan Gamhna, Gunna, CDP, 1989, det. PDS, **CGE**; by Arileod farm track, 157548, JWC, 1986, det. AMcGS, **E**; W of Arnabost, 207606, JWC, 1987, det. AMcGS.

Subsp. *trichosoma*: Cliad Farm, 206597, JWC, 1984, det. AMcGS, **E**.

Pilularia globulifera   Pillwort   T 04
Shallow water in lochans, *Menyanthes* swamps and poached ground by water. Found only at the eastern end of Tiree: L. an t-Sleibh Dheirg, 075483, IAW, 1947, and later observers up to BSBI, 1990; the neighbouring lochan at 075484, CDP & NFS, 1989; L. Mointeich Mhoir, 073491, ACJ, 1984, **BM**, and BSBI, 1990; pool SW of Dun Beag, 075492, BSBI, 1990; L. an Duin, Millton, 085477, BSBI, 1990.

[*Pimpinella saxifraga*   Burnet-saxifrage

Roadside grassland past Fish Gate, 235629, BSB, 1988. This record was mapped by Palmer & Bratton (1995) but there are no other records for NW Scotland, and it is best regarded as an error.]

Pinguicula lusitanica   Pale Butterwort   T 93,94,04; C 15,25,26

Fairly uncommon in flushes and bogs, usually on moorlands.

Pinguicula vulgaris   Common Butterwort   All except T 05, G 15

Much more frequent than *P. lusitanica*, but also predominantly in moorland habitats.

Pinus contorta   Lodgepole Pine   C 15,25,26

Planted in several places.

Pinus sylvestris   Scots Pine   T 94; C 25

Planted, at Mannal, 94, and Arinagour, 25.

Plantago coronopus   Buck's-horn Plantain   All

Very frequent on machair and coastal turf throughout.

Plantago lanceolata   Ribwort Plantain   All

Abundant in all habitats, particularly in improved and ruderal situations.

Plantago major   Greater Plantain   All

Abundant in all habitats, particularly in improved and ruderal situations. Subsp. *intermedia* has been recorded once, at the edge of depressions and rock pools at Urvaig, 05, DAP & CDP, 1997.

Plantago maritima   Sea Plantain   All

Frequent in saltmarshes and in turf on rocks by the sea.

[*Plantago media*   Hoary Plantain

Recorded from Tiree Aerodrome, 002456, TD (Dargie 1993), with weedy species, but presumably in error for *P. lanceolata*.]

Platanthera bifolia   Lesser Butterfly-orchid   T 94; C all

Rare in moorland with very few recent records: Cnoc Bhirceapol, 9644, BSBI, 1990; L. a'Chlair, 9844, BSBI, 1990; Lochan a'Chuirn, 15, JWC, 1987; Druim Buidhe marsh, 1554, CJC, 1998; Ballyhaugh, 175582, CJC, 1998; near Cliad, 1960, JWC, 1991; L. Airigh Meall Bhreide, 25, BKC, 1987+; L. a'Mhill Aird, 26F, JWC, 1987.

Platanthera chlorantha   Greater Butterfly-orchid   T 94,04

Recorded recently from moorland: S of L. Stanail, 9744, BSBI, 1990; Vaul, 04P, BSBI, 1990. The only other record is from Ceann a'Mhara (Macvicar 1898).

Poa annua   Annual Meadow-grass   All

Widespread everywhere.

Poa humilis   Spreading Meadow-grass   T all; C 15,(25),26

Widespread, and probably under-recorded, in grassy situations, particularly machair.

***Poa palustris**   Swamp Meadow-grass   T 94,04; C (15),(26)

HH recorded this plant as "local and always amongst Irises; Arnabost, Gallanach etc., on Coll, and very common between Urvaig and Salum, Tiree". There is a specimen at **K** from Creag an Fhireoin, 15, HHH, 1.6.1939, det. CEH, 11.2.1940. This specimen is very poor, very brown, lacking paleas and almost all lemmas. What remains is almost certainly *P. palustris.* J. Heslop Harrison (1949) listed it as abundant in a large *Iris pseudacorus* bed E of Gott Manse, 04. Since then it has been recorded three times: S end of L. Bhasapol, 973465, DAP, 1990; An Fhaodhail, 015448, PW, 1983; NE of Salum, 068492, DAP, 1990. We have accepted all these records but confirmation is desirable.

Poa pratensis   Smooth Meadow-grass   T 93,94; C 15,25,26

There are scattered records of *P. pratensis,* but it is less common than the closely related *P. humilis.*

Poa trivialis   Rough Meadow-grass   All except T 05, C 16

Widespread and fairly frequent.

Polygala serpyllifolia   Heath Milkwort   T 93,94,04; (G); C 15,25,26

Fairly frequent on cliffs and moorland.

Polygala vulgaris   Common Milkwort   T 93,94,04; G 05,15; C all

As widespread as the preceding, but considerably more frequent on Coll.

Polygonum arenastrum   Equal-leaved Knotgrass   T (94),04,05; C 15,25,26

In trampled places, such as tracks and gateways. Certainly under-recorded; of the ten records, seven were made by DAP & CDP in 1997.

Polygonum aviculare   Knotgrass   T 94,04; G 15; C 15,25,26

In similar places to the preceding, not frequently recorded.

Polygonum boreale   Northern Knotgrass   T 93,94,04

A weedy species, first recorded in 1989. Potato field, Hynish Farm, 981389, BSBI, 1990, det. CDP, **CGE**; sandy beaches, Clachan Mor, 981478, JWC, 1990, det. JRA, **E**, and Aird Mor, 993477, CDP & NFS, 1989, det. JRA, **CGE**; The Reef, 006449, BHT, 1990, det. BTS, **GLAM**, and 012452, CJC, 1995; weed in potato beds, Ruaig, 070477, DAP & CDP, 1997, det. JRA, **CGE**. Possibly still under-recorded.

Polygonum oxyspermum   Ray's Knotgrass   T 94,04; C (15),25

Occasional on sandy shores where it usually occurs in small quantity. The only recent records are: Traigh nan Gilean, 938420, DAP & CDP, 1997; Balephuil Bay, 945407, CDP, 1997; Traigh Bhagh, 018439, CJC, 1995; Traigh Bhalla, Vaul, 056485, CDP, 1997; Caolas-an-eilean, 221557, DAP, CDP *et al.*, 1997.

Polypodium interjectum   Intermediate Polypody
                                       T (93),(94),04,(05); C 15,25,26

Occasional in rock crevices and ravines; probably the more frequent of the two *Polypodium* species, but with only ten records in total. There are recent records of *P. vulgare sens. lat.* from all except T 05 and C 16. Many plants in exposed crevices are only tiny.

Polypodium interjectum* × *vulgare (P. × mantoniae)   T 94; C 15

Ceann a'Mhara, 94, DAP & CDP, det. RHR, 1997, **CGE**; Coll, 15, JWC, det. AMcGS, 1987.

Polypodium vulgare   Polypody   T 94; C 15,25,26

Occasional in rock crevices and ravines; recorded seven times.

Polystichum aculeatum   Hard Shield-fern   C (26)

L. a'Mhill Aird, BSBI, 1967. The only record, published by Duncan (1968a,b). Frequent along the west coast of Scotland.

Populus balsamifera × *deltoides (P. × jackii)   Balm-of-Gilead   C 25

Planted at The Lodge, Arinagour, 25, BSB, 1988.

Populus tremula   Aspen   C (15),25,26

Rare, and only occasional in gorges on the south coast of Coll, and on ledges and around rocky lochans in the NE of the island. Self-sown plants occur in fenced ground near Arinagour.

Potamogeton

Unless stated, all records cited below have been made by CDP and/or NFS in 1989 and 1990 and most of these are supported by voucher specimens in **CGE**. All SNHLS records are based on specimens collected in 1994 which have been confirmed by CDP and will be deposited in **E**. J.W. Heslop Harrison's (1949) ecological account of this genus in the Hebrides is still of considerable interest.

Potamogeton alpinus Red Pondweed C 25

Macvicar collected this species from Coll in 1896, without specifying the locality or publishing the record. Subsequently there is only a field record from a ditch in fen N of Arinagour, 223584, BSB, 1988. We have been unable to refind the plant and suspect an error in the grid reference, as the ditches here run through saltmarsh rather than fen.

Potamogeton berchtoldii Small Pondweed T 94,04; C 15,25,26

Uncommon in ditches, pools and lochs. It is absent from the machair lochs of Tiree (though present in other coastal and moorland sites), but on Coll it was found by SNHLS in 1994 in three machair lochs in 15 (L. nan Easgannan, Lochan a'Chuirn, L. Ballyhaugh) as well as two moorland sites (L. Cliad, 207589, and L. an t-Sagairt, 250610).

Potamogeton coloratus Fen Pondweed T 94,04; C (15),(25),26

A rare plant of ditches, streams, lochs and pools. At a few sites the water shows few signs of base-enrichment, but the species is most frequent and vigorous in the most calcareous sites. On Tiree it is known from L. a'Phuill, 957425, SNHLS, 1994; near Balephetrish, 008462, TD, 1993; N end of An Fhaodhail, 0146; L. Riaghain, 0346-0347; L. na Buaile, 0344 and the long, thin lake N of L. Ghrianal, 038481, but it is no longer present on Balephetrish Hill, where it was known to HH and UKD, 1968, **BM**. It was found by Cadbury & Cowie (1998) in small ponds where turves had been removed to construct temporary dams, An Fhaodhail, 012462. Recorded also from near L. a'Chlair, 985444, TD, 1993, and but we have not accepted this record without confirmation. Rarer on Coll, where it was formerly recorded from Lochan a'Chuirn, 1152, by HH and UKD, 1967, **BM**, and L. an Duin, 2157, SMM, 1896, **BM**, and still persists in the stream at Gallanach, 217608.

Potamogeton filiformis Slender-leaved Pondweed T (93),94,04; C 15

Coastal lakes, pools and sluggish streams, especially where the substrate is sandy. Frequent on Tiree in the larger lochs and in the streams and pools of the An Fhaodhail complex, but on Coll confined to Lochan

Seileach, 119518, and Lochan a'Chuirn, 119523, at the sandy western end of the island and a clear rock pool near Calgary Point, 109526, where it grows with *Myriophyllum spicatum, Ruppia maritima, Chara aspera* and *C. hispida*. For a map of recent records, see Fig. 6.

Potamogeton filiformis × pectinatus (P. × suecicus)   Swedish Pondweed
T 94,04

Locally dominant in two sites on Tiree. Known from L. a'Phuill and nearby ditches, 94, but particularly abundant in the outflow stream Abhainn a'Bheidhe, where it was discovered by HH. The other site is the An Fhaodhail complex, 04, where it was collected by Macvicar in 1897, and is especially abundant in the central stream and the large, shallow backwater at Poll Orisgal (Preston *et al.* 1999). An Fhaodhail is remarkable for the presence of at least six clones of the hybrid; only one or two were detected at ten other British sites (including L. a'Phuill) studied by Hollingsworth *et al.* (1996).

Potamogeton gramineus   Various-leaved Pondweed   T 94,04; C 15,25,26

Present in most of the more base-rich lochs on Tiree and the western end of Coll. It is capable of withstanding marked fluctuations in water level in the turlough-like machair lochs of W Coll, and in 1989 terrestrial rosettes were present at L. nan Easgannan, 118524, some 5 metres from the water's edge. Rare in central and eastern Coll, where it is only known from L. Cliad, 2058, SNHLS, 1994; L. a'Mhill Aird, 231606; L. a'Mhill Aird Bhig, 233602. For a map of recent records, see Fig. 6.

Potamogeton gramineus × natans (P. × sparganiifolius)
Ribbon-leaved Pondweed   T 04

Discovered at L. Riaghain, 04, by UKD, 1968, **BM**. Here it grows not only as scattered plants in the loch itself (where both parents occur) but also as dwarf plants in a broad, very shallow stream flowing through the calcareous fen on the S side.

Potamogeton gramineus × perfoliatus (P. × nitens)
Bright-leaved Pondweed   T 94,04; C (15)

A scarce hybrid, recorded from four of the larger, base-rich lochs on Tiree: L. a'Phuill, 94; L. Bhasapol, 9646; L. an Eilein, 9843; L. Riaghain, 0346. A specimen from HH's locality on Coll, L. Ballyhaugh, 15, was confirmed by JED & GT but the hybrid has not been seen since at this well-surveyed site.

Potamogeton natans   Broad-leaved Pondweed   T 94,04; C all

Frequent and often abundant in ditches, streams, pools and lakes. For a map of recent records, see Fig. 8.

Potamogeton pectinatus   Fennel Pondweed   T 94,04; C 16,26

Recorded from base-rich lakes on Tiree: L. Bhasapol, 9747; L. a'Phuill, 94; L. Earblaig, 9446, SNHLS; L. an Eilein, 9843; L. Dubh a'Gharraidh Fail, 0248 and the An Fhaodhail complex, 04; also in a cliff-top rock pool at Am Beannan Ruadh, 031490. Known from two rock pools on Coll, at 193603, JWC, 1991, and 215617, PFB, 1989, both det. CDP.

Potamogeton perfoliatus   Perfoliate Pondweed   T 94; C 15,25,26

Known from three large, base-rich lochs in W Tiree: L. Bhasapol, 94; L. a'Phuill, 94; L. an Eilein, 9843. On Coll found in a similar site, L. Ballyhaugh, 15, but also in more acidic sites: L. Cliad, 25; L. Urbhaig, 2357; L. an t-Sagairt, 2560. The distribution is similar to that of *P. gramineus* but *P. perfoliatus* is intolerant of desiccation and is therefore absent from the smaller lochs over sand. For a map of recent records, see Fig. 5.

Potamogeton polygonifolius   Bog Pondweed   All

Abundant in shallow water in ditches, flushes, marshes and at the edge of lochs, occurring throughout the islands but especially frequent in the peaty moorlands. For a map of recent records, see Fig. 8.

[*Potamogeton praelongus*   Long-stalked Pondweed

With *Eriocaulon* in a lochan E of Moss, 969446, TD (Dargie 1993); stream N of L. a'Phuill, 958427, TD (Dargie 1993). We have accepted neither record without a specimen. The species is scattered in the Inner Hebrides, but these are atypical habitats for a plant of deep, mesotrophic waters and LF was unable to refind it at 969446 in 1999.]

Potamogeton pusillus   Lesser Pondweed   T 94,04

This replaces *P. berchtoldii* in the two largest machair lochs and in the streams and pools of the An Fhaodhail complex on Tiree: L. a'Phuill, its outflow Abhainn a'Bheidhe and nearby ditches, 94; L. Bhasapol, 94; An Fhaodhail, 04.

Potamogeton rutilus   Shetland Pondweed   T 94; C 15

Not discovered on the islands until 1968, but now known from three mesotrophic lochs: L. an Eilein, 9843, UKD, 1968, **BM**, PMH, 1993, **LTR** and SNHLS, 1994, **E**; L. a'Chlair, 983445, CK & MARK, 1990, det. CDP, **CGE** and RNE & PMH, 1993; L. Ballyhaugh, 176581, CDP &

NFS, 1989 and SNHLS, 1994, **E**. The history of this rare species on the islands epitomises its history in Scotland, where it was once thought to be exceptionally rare but has been found in several new localities in recent years.

Potentilla anglica or *erecta* × *reptans (P.* × *mixta)*   Hybrid Cinquefoil
C (25)

In grass, Craigdarroch, Arinagour, JWC, 1986, det. BH, **E**.

Potentilla anserina   Silverweed   All

Widespread and frequent on shingle, and in rocky and waste places.

Potentilla erecta   Tormentil   All except T 05

Plentiful on moorlands, cliffs and other acid places. Subsp. *erecta* has been recorded once, Arinagour, 2256, LF, 1997, but probably occurs throughout.

Potentilla palustris   Marsh Cinquefoil   T 93,94,04; (G); C 15,25,26

Common in bogs throughout the islands.

Potentilla reptans   Creeping Cinquefoil   T 93,94,04; (G); C (15),(25),(26)

Rarely recorded, from waste places, with ten records in all, and only three of these recent: Ben Hynish, 93, LF & RS, 1988; Sandaig, 9343, DAP & CDP, 1997; E of Balephetrish, 04, BSBI, 1990.

Potentilla sterilis   Barren Strawberry   C (26)

The only record is from HH " on a rock ledge near Sorisdale". There are scattered records from the W coast of Scotland.

Primula vulgaris   Primrose   All except T 05

Locally common in rocky, well-drained places, and on machair and grassy banks.

Prunella vulgaris   Selfheal   All

Frequent and widespread, especially in damp places on machair.

****Prunus avium**   Wild Cherry   C (15)

"Planted", 15, BSBI, 1967, without precise location.

Prunus spinosa   Blackthorn   C 15,(25)

HH recorded this as "very rare; on a large rock not far from Arinagour, and in a gorge near Rudha Fasachd". The only other record is for two small bushes S of church, Arinagour, 15, KPB, 1988. There are scattered records on Mull, in Ardnamurchan and on Canna.

Pseudorchis albida   Small-white Orchid   C (15),(25)

Only recorded twice: near Crossapol, 15, HH, and between church and shore, 25, Arinagour, AW, 1985.

*Pseudotsuga menziesii   Douglas Fir   C 25

Planted, Arinagour, BSB, 1988.

Pteridium aquilinum sens. lat.   Bracken   All except G 05

Frequent on Coll, but local on Tiree; HH's comment that it is "abundant throughout the islands" no longer applies to the latter, if ever it did.

Puccinellia maritima   Common Saltmarsh-grass
                                              T 93,94,04; G 15; C 15,25,26

Quite common on saltmarshes, but not in every one.

Pyrola media   Intermediate Wintergreen   C (25)

Only recorded by HH: "one patch on the banks of Loch Airidh Meall Bhreide". Elsewhere found on Mull, Eigg and on Ardnamurchan.

Pyrola minor   Common Wintergreen   C (25)

Only recorded by HH: "on the side of the Arinagour, Arnabost road". Scattered along the west coast of Scotland.

?**Quercus petraea*   Sessile Oak   C (25)

HH recorded this "on rocky flats near the Dairy Loch [L. Airigh Meall Bhreide], but much rarer than *Q. robur*". It was listed from 25 without precise locality by AMcGS, 1959.

?**Quercus petraea* × *robur (Q.* × *rosacea)*   C 25

One plant self sown at Arinagour, 221573, CDP *et al.*, 1997, det. PDS, **CGE**.

?**Quercus robur*   Pedunculate Oak   C (15),25

L. Ballyhaugh, 15, JWC, 1985; Craigdarroch, Arinagour, 25, JWC, 1983; The Lodge, Arinagour, planted, DAP, CDP *et al.*, 1997. HH recorded this as "clearly native" along the west shore of L. Eatharna, and on rocks to the east of the Dairy Loch (L. Airigh Meall Bhreide).

SPECIES LIST: VASCULAR PLANTS

Radiola linoides   Allseed   T 94; C (25)

E of Hough, 957456, AMcGS & BHT, 1990; locally abundant on dried sand and mud flats, N end of L. Stanail, 9745, BSBI, 1990, **GLAM**. The only record for Coll is from Cliad district, HH.

Ranunculus acris   Meadow Buttercup   All

Very common everywhere, except on the moorlands.

Ranunculus aquatilis   Common Water-crowfoot   T 94; C (16),26

The few records of this species come from mesotrophic sites, often near the sea: L. an Eilein, 9843, BSBI, 1990, det. SDW; Cliad Burn, 1960, JWC, 1983, det. NTHH, **E**; near Cliad Farm, 25, BSBI, 1967; NW of Arnabost, 2060, JWC, 1987. HH's record from An Fhaodhail has been deleted in view of probable confusion with other species. TD recorded it at least nine times from Tiree in 1993, but we consider that these were probably errors for *R. trichophyllus.*

Ranunculus baudotii   Brackish Water-crowfoot T 94,04; (G); C (15)

Rare, in streams and pools near the sea. On Tiree it has been confirmed from five localities: the exit stream from L. a'Phuill, 94, An Fhaodhail, 04, and three lochans and pools near Vaul, 04. There are records from many more sites by TD in 1993 but we have been cautious in accepting records in this difficult subgenus. On Coll the only record since 1968 is Lochan a'Chuirn, 1152, AW, 1986, det. SDW, **E**. Macvicar (1898) recorded this species from a loch 20 feet above sea-level. For a map of recent records, see Fig. 9.

Ranunculus baudotii × *trichophyllus (R.* × *segretii)*   T 94

Larger of two pools E of L. na Faing, 968421, NFS & SDW, 1990, det. SDW, **GLAM**.

Ranunculus bulbosus   Bulbous Buttercup   T 93,94,04,(05); G 15; C all

Common on dunes and machair.

Ranunculus ficaria   Lesser Celandine   T 93,94,04,(05); G 05; C (15),25,26

Described by HH as "more or less abundant on rock ledges and at the base of cliffs". In recent years this spring-flowering species has probably been under-recorded. Subsp. *ficaria* has been recorded from T (93),94, G 15 and C 26 and is probably the only subspecies present.

Ranunculus flammula   Lesser Spearwort   All

Widespread and very common in all wetter places. Macvicar's (1897c) record of subsp. *scoticus* has not been confirmed.

[*Ranunculus fluitans*   River Water-crowfoot

Recorded by HH, from a pool W of Crossapol Bay, C 15. The taxonomy of this group has been revised since 1940, and the occurrence of *R. fluitans* as currently understood is most unlikely.]

[*Ranunculus hederaceus*   Ivy-leaved Crowfoot

There are records from Clachan Mor, 94, DC, 1990 and An Fhaodhail, 017442, PW, 1983 (cf Wormell 1989) but no specimens have been seen, nor was either record checked by an expert in this difficult subgenus.]

Ranunculus lingua   Greater Spearwort   T 94

Barrapol, NW of L. a'Phuill, 94, MGBH, 1990, **GLAM**. One of only two records from the west of Scotland.

Ranunculus repens   Creeping Buttercup   All

Common and widespread on roadsides, cultivated fields, gardens and other ruderal sites.

Ranunculus sceleratus   Celery-leaved Buttercup   T 94, C 15

Clachan Mor, 984477, DC, 1990; beach at Crossapol, HH, a site where one plant was seen both by BSBI in 1990 and at 128531 by DAP & CDP in 1997. There are no other records.

Ranunculus trichophyllus   Thread-leaved Water-crowfoot
                                        T 93,94,04; C 15,16,25

The common fine-leaved *Ranunculus*, fairly widespread in shallow water in areas influenced by the machair. For a map of recent records, see Fig. 6.

Raphanus raphanistrum subsp. *raphanistrum*
                                        Wild Radish   T 94,04; C (15),(25),26

Formerly common as an arable weed, now rarely recorded, though seen twice in 1997.

[*Rhinanthus angustifolius*   Greater Yellow-rattle

Recorded as "scattered on Coll and Tiree" by HH. Though this has declined nationally it is almost entirely eastern and might have been confused with the very variable *R. minor*.]

Rhinanthus minor   Yellow-rattle   T 93,94,04; C 15,25,26

Fairly widespread in machair, and occasionally in arable fields. Little attention has been paid to the subspecies since HH but the following records are available:

Subsp. *minor*: NW of Arnabost, 202609, JWC, 1987, det. HJN.

Subsp. *monticola*: Heanish, 04, UKD, 1968, **BM**; turf over rocks by Poll Orisgal, An Fhaodhail, 015457, CDP, 1997, det. PDS, **CGE**; machair SE of Hogh Bay, 15, UKD, 1967, **BM**; L. a'Mhill Aird area, 26, HH.

Subsp. *stenophyllus*: edge of ditch SW of Balephuil, 961405, DAP & CDP, 1997, det. PDS, **CGE**; The Reef, 04, UKD, 1968, **BM**; bank of stream over dunes SE of Ben Feall, 147548, DAP & CDP, 1997, det. PDS, **CGE**.

Rhynchospora alba   White Beak-sedge   C 25,26

Recorded by HH as "common on the Coll moorlands, although somewhat local", there are very few localised records. The record in 15 mapped by Perring & Walters (1962) was only included on the strength of the above comment, and should be deleted. Recent records are L. Boidheach, 201568, NFS, 1990; near L. an Duin, 209581, CDP & NFS, 1989; L. a'Mhill Aird, 26F, HJN *et al.*, 1987.

***Ribes nigrum**   Black Currant   T 04; C 25

Rare, as a garden escape or relic.

***Ribes rubrum**   Red Currant   C (26)

No locality, 26, BSBI, 1967.

***Ribes uva-crispa**   Gooseberry   C 26

Ruins, Sorisdale, JWC, 1988.

Rorippa microphylla   Narrow-fruited Water-cress   G 05,15; C (15)

Only recorded from Gunna, 05 and 15, JWC & HJN, 1987, and from Crossapol Bay, 15, BSBI, 1967, **DEE**.

Rorippa microphylla × nasturtium-aquaticum (R. × sterilis)
          Hybrid Water-cress   T 04; C 16,25,26

There are records from four localities: Am Beannan Ruadh, 035490, CK, MARK & CDP, 1990; Cliad Burn, 199600 and 200599, CDP, 1990; Gallanach, 217608, CDP, 1989; all det. TCGR, **CGE**.

Rorippa nasturtium-aquaticum   Water-cress   T 93,94,04; C 15,25,26

Quite common in streams and ditches, especially near the coast. It probably occurs throughout Coll and Tiree as there are records of the aggregate from all squares.

***Rorippa sylvestris**   Creeping Yellow-cress   C (26)

By silage shed, Cornaigbeg, BKC & KAHC, det. AMcGS, 1986, **E**.

Rosa

With the exception of *Rosa pimpinellifolia*, all the roses on the islands belong to the critical Section *Caninae*. This was a group which J.W. Heslop Harrison had studied in detail, and with K.B. Blackburn he was one of the biologists who discovered the unusual breeding system of the caninoid roses in the early 1920s. Heslop Harrison & Bolton (1938) reviewed the genus in the Inner and Outer Hebrides and the 1941 Flora provides a detailed account of the roses of Coll and Tiree according to the taxonomic system of the time.

The rarity of roses on Tiree was noted by Macvicar (1897a) who reported that "the only Rosae seen were three dwarf bushes, clinging to the face of a rock and too immature to be determined". In 1997 one of our aims was to review the roses of the islands in the light of the recent taxonomic revision of Graham & Primavesi (1993). However, we were unable to make much progress as we failed to find any roses on Tiree and on Coll we only detected two small populations. The small populations which, even if found, may be depauperate and lack flowers and fruits also handicap the study of the genus in the Outer Hebrides (Pankhurst & Mullin 1991). A more single-minded attempt to refind roses at the localities cited by HH would be worthwhile, as if successful it would clarify the taxa present and if unsuccessful it would document the effects of continuous grazing pressure on the trees and shrubs of the islands. In the meantime we have attempted to equate the taxa reported by HH with those currently recognised, although this is not easy in the absence of any published concordance between the two systems. Records of *Rosa* sp. or *Rosa canina* agg. have been disregarded. Until the appearance of Stace (1991) and Graham & Primavesi (1993) recorders from the 1950s onwards tended to identify caninoid roses only as far as these broadly defined aggregates, which have been recorded since 1950 from T 93,(94) and C 15,25,26. All the species in Section *Caninae* must be regarded as under-recorded.

Rosa caesia subsp. *glauca*   Glaucous Dog-rose   T (94); C 15

There are two confirmed records: marsh near Heylipol church, Barrapol, 94, UKD, 1968, det. ALP, **BM**; three plants growing with *Hedera helix* on a small cliff at Ben Feall, 146547, DAP & CDP, conf. ALP, 1997, **CGE**. Plants attributed to the *R. glaucophylla* aggregate by HH presumably refer to *R. caesia* or its hybrids; they were reported from Beinn Hough, 94, a ravine near Balephetrish, 04, and near Ben Hogh, 15, the coast between Arinagour and Eilean Ornsay, 25, Ceann-a-Bhaigh, 2463, and near Cornaig and Cornaigbeg, 26. An aberrant form of *R. coriifolia* was also reported by HH, from rocks NE of Gallanach, 26; this name is a synonym of *R. caesia* subsp. *caesia* but there seems little point in speculating on the identity of Heslop Harrison's plant.

Rosa caesia subsp. **glauca** × **pimpinellifolia (R.** × **margerisonii)** T 04

04, KT, 1996, det. ALP (as the cross with *R. caesia* as the female parent).

Rosa caesia subsp. **glauca** × **sherardii** C 15

Boulders above shore between L. Breachacha and L. Gortan, 164530, DAP & CDP, 1997, det. ALP, **CGE**.

Rosa canina Dog-rose C 25,(26)

Macvicar (1897a) used this name in the aggregate sense. Listed by HH from rock ledges at four sites in eastern Coll, near L. Cliad, 25, L. a'Mhill Aird, 26, L. Fada, 26, and S of Gallanach, 26, and subsequently from 25 by BSB, 1988. It was also recorded on Tiree from Carnan Mor, 970406, TD (Dargie 1993) but there is no voucher specimen and we have not, therefore, accepted this record.

Rosa mollis Soft Downy-rose C 26

Only reported from NE Coll. "Rare on a stream side near Torastan, Coll" according to HH, who reassuringly referred their material to var. *typica*, and subsequently recorded from Sorisdale by BSBI, 1989.

Rosa mollis × **pimpinellifolia (R.** × **sabinii)** T (04)

Near Caoles, 04, UKD, 1968, det. ALP, **BM**.

Rosa pimpinellifolia Burnet Rose T 93,94,(04); G 15; C 15,25,26

Occasional and usually in small quantity on coastal and inland rock outcrops, but not recorded from sand dunes.

Rosa pimpinellifolia × **sherardii (R.** × **involuta)** C (26)

HH reported "one or two bushes on the side of the stream flowing from Toraston toward A Chroic". This is a widespread hybrid which is known from the Outer Hebrides (Graham & Primavesi 1993) and there seems little reason to doubt the record from Coll, even in the absence of a voucher specimen.

*****Rosa rubiginosa** Sweet-briar C (25)

Behind hotel, Arinagour, JWC, 1986, det. AMcGS & ALP, **E**.

Rosa sherardii Sherard's Downy-rose T (94),04; C 25,(26)

HH considered that *R. sherardii* var. *typica* was "a little more abundant than most rose forms on Coll and Tiree", recording it from Beinn Hough and Balephetrish, Tiree, and many rock ledges in eastern Coll. It has subsequently been recorded from Balephetrish, 04, JWC, 1982, and Carnan Mora, 212584, BSB, 1988. Our record of the hybrid between *R. caesia* subsp. *glauca* and *R. sherardii* at 164530 was based on a specimen collected in driving rain from just one of several bushes on a sea cliff and amongst nearby boulders; we did not examine the bushes closely in the field but all resembled *R. sherardii* superficially and some of the other bushes might actually be the species rather than the hybrid.

Rubus Bramble

With the exception of *Rubus idaeus*, all the species recorded from Coll and Tiree are bramble microspecies in Subgenus *Rubus* Section *Rubus* (*Rubus fruticosus* agg.). Like other woody species, brambles are restricted to cliffs, rock outcrops and enclosed ground by houses where they escape grazing, and are more frequent on Coll than Tiree. They are recorded from T 93, 94, 04 and C 15, 25, 26. Records of four microspecies were published by Macvicar (1897a,b) from Coll (he was unable to find any on Tiree) and HH provided a detailed account. Recent records are based to a large extent on the collections of JWC and the determinations of AMcGS. Nomenclature follows Edees & Newton (1988)

We have not accepted the records published by Macvicar or HH unless there is a confirmed record for v.c. 103 in Edees & Newton (1988). Some of the unconfirmed species are included in square brackets in the main species list but the following species listed by HH are either very unlikely to be correct (as Coll and Tiree lies well outside the known distribution of the species as it is currently understood) or they are dubious names which cannot be equated to species currently recognised: *R. adenanthus, R. adenolobus, R. nitidus, R. oxyanchus, R. rotundifolius, R. schlechtendalii* var. *anglicus, R. sulcatus.*

Most of the species accepted below are taxa which are widespread in Britain (*R. nemoralis, R. polyanthemus*) or have northerly distributions here (*R. latifolius, R. mucronulatus, R. septentrionalis*) but *R. dumnoniensis* has a western distribution, *R. conjungens* is a southern species with scattered outliers further north and *R. subinermoides* is also a species of SE England but with a second centre in western Scotland.

Rubus conjungens T (04); C (25)

Recorded by HH from rocks at An Cnap, 04, and mapped in 25 by Edees & Newton (1988).

Rubus dumnoniensis   C (15),25,26

Recorded from Coll by Macvicar (1897a,b) on the authority of W. Moyle Rogers and considered by HH to be one of the most plentiful brambles on that island. Subsequent records bear this out: Caoles, 15, JWC, 1986; Craigdarroch, Arinagour, 25, JWC, 1984 and 1987+; Sorisdale, 271635, JWC, 1988, det. AMcGS.

Rubus idaeus   Raspberry   T (04); C 15,(26)

A rare plant of rock outcrops and cliff ledges. HH recorded it from a coastal site, An Cnap, on Tiree and inland in E Coll. The only recent record is from the coast between L. Breachacha and L. Gortan, 15R, DAP, CDP *et al.*, 1997.

Rubus latifolius   T 93

On two ungrazed rock ledges between Hynish and West Hynish, 965387 and 969389, JG & PT, 1990, det. AMcGS but material inadequate for absolutely certain identification.

[*Rubus leptothyrsos*

Listed from Coll by Macvicar (1897a,b) as *R. danicus*, det. W. Moyle Rogers. Not reported subsequently and with no confirmed record from v.c. 103 in Edees & Newton (1988) but this is a widespread species in Scotland which might well occur.]

Rubus mucronulatus   T (04); C 26

Recorded as "not uncommon" on Coll by HH and subsequently from both islands: Balephetrish Hill, 04, JWC, 1982, and a small rocky gorge at Cornaigbeg, 241638, JWC, 1988, det. AMcGS.

Rubus nemoralis   C (15),25,26

Another frequent species on Coll, known to Macvicar (as *R. villicaulis* var. *selmeri*) and HH and more recently found at: Ballyhaugh and Caoles, 15, JWC, 1986; Craigdarroch, Arinagour, 25, JWC, 1984, E, and 1987+; along burn, Gallanach, 218604, JWC, 1988; amongst rocks, Cornaigbeg, 239629, JWC, 1988, det. AMcGS; Dun Morbhaidh area, 234631, JWC, 1987; by cottage and ruins, Sorisdale, 26, JWC, 1986, det. AMcGS.

[*Rubus plicatus*

Listed from Coll by Macvicar (1897a,b), det. W. Moyle Rogers. Not reported subsequently but this is a widespread species in Britain which is known from Mull and might well occur on Coll.]

Rubus polyanthemus C (15),25,26

HH thought that this was "very common and widespread on Coll" and it has subsequently been found at: Beg a'Mhonaidh near Broadhills, 15, JWC, 1986; Craigdarroch garden, Arinagour, 25, JWC, 1986; Arnabost area, 25, BSB, 1988; single bush amongst rocks at Clachard, 208606, JWC, 1988. All JMC's records were determined by AMcGS.

[*Rubus radula*

Amongst rocks, An Cnap, 04, HH. There is no confirmed record from v.c. 103 (Edees & Newton 1988) but this is a widespread species which occurs in Skye and the Outer Hebrides and the HH record could well be correct.]

Rubus septentrionalis T 04; C (25),26

Druim a'Choirce, 04, JWC, 1984; Dun Mor a'Chaolais, 083476, PT, 1990, det. AMcGS; Craigdarroch garden, Arinagour, 25, JWC, 1984, **E**, and 1987+; along the burn at Gallanach, 218604, JWC, 1988, det. AMcGS; amongst rocks at Cornaigbeg, 241629, JWC, 1988, det. AMcGS.

Rubus subinermoides C (15)

By bridge, Allt Mor, 15, JWC, 1986, **E**.

Rumex acetosa Common Sorrel All

Very common, especially in cultivated and arable fields, and on roadsides.

Rumex acetosella Sheep's Sorrel T 94,04,(05); G 05,15; C 15,25,26

Common and widespread.

**Rumex conglomeratus* Clustered Dock T 04; C (15)

On Tiree known from Millton, 085475, SJL, 1990; also recorded three times by TD (Dargie 1993) but probably in error. On Coll there is also one record: a few plants in damp hollow of cart-track near Caoles, 126527, JWC, 1986, **E**.

Rumex crispus Curled Dock All

Common and widespread on dunes and rocks, on roadsides and in fields. Subsp. *crispus* was recorded five times at coastal and inland sites in 1997 from T 04 and C 15,25. Subsp. *littoreus* was recorded by the coast four times in 1997, from T 94 and C 15,25.

Rumex crispus × *obtusifolius (R.* × *pratensis)* T 94

Clachan Mor, 984477, AW, det. AMcGS, 1990.

[*Rumex longifolius*   Northern Dock

Recorded from a meadow at Heylipol, 980425, TD (Dargie 1993) but we have assumed that this is a mistake.]

Rumex obtusifolius   Broad-leaved Dock   T 93,94,04; G 15; C 15,25,26

Frequent in many ruderal and cultivated places.

Ruppia maritima   Beaked Tasselweed   T 94,04; G 05; C 15,25,26

Not uncommon in pools in saltmarshes, or amongst rocks in the spray zone. For a map of recent records, see Fig. 9.

Sagina maritima   Sea Pearlwort   T (93),(94),04; G 15; C 15

Rare, amongst rocks on the shore. The only recent records are Port Ban, 014482, SJL, 1990; Scarinish, 04, AMcGS, 1990; Soy Gunna, 1051, BSBI, 1989; Breachacha Castle, 163541, SJL, 1989; W end of Coll, 15, CDP & NFS, 1989.

Sagina nodosa   Knotted Pearlwort   T 93,04,05; (G); C 15,25,26

Occasional, but locally plentiful on damp sand in dune slacks and in salt-marshes.

Sagina procumbens   Procumbent Pearlwort   All

Abundant in many places, including natural habitats such as shaded rocks as well as trampled ground.

Sagina subulata   Heath Pearlwort   T (93),04; C (15),(16),(25),26

"In bare and other places on moorlands; scattered thinly on Coll and Tiree" HH, but with only two recent records: Vaul, 04P, BSBI, 1990; near Gallanach, 2160, JWC & HJN, 1987.

Salicornia agg.   Glasswort   T 04; C (15),25

Very uncommon, and found only at NE of Salum, 073493, SJL, 1990; Soa, 075471, SJL, 1990; Millton, 085475, CJC, 1983 and SJL, 1990; L. Eatharna, 225581, SJL, 1990. HH recorded *S. ramosissima* from Caoles (15), but this has not been refound and should be treated as a dubious record. Macvicar (1898) recorded *S europaea* (as *S. herbacea*) from Heanish saltmarsh, 04, but the presence of this species also requires confirmation; it is, however, the only species recorded from Mull.

*Salix alba 'Britzensis'   Golden Willow   C 26

Flourishing in a sandpit dump at Cliad, 26, JWC, 1988, det. RDM, from cuttings thrown out from The Lodge, Arinagour.

Salix aurita   Eared Willow   T 93,(94),(04); G 05; C all

Much the most frequent of the shrubby willows. On Tiree it has only been recorded since 1970 from Port Snoig, 968387, PT, 1990, det. AMcGS, **GLAM**, and roadsides near L. an t-Sleibh Dheirg and Balephetrish, 04, JWC, 1982, but it is much more frequent on Coll.

Salix aurita × ***cinerea*** subsp. ***oleifolia (S.*** × ***multinervis)***   C (26)

"Very rare on an island in Loch Ghillecaluim on Coll" HH. This is "a very common hybrid, found wherever the parent species occur" (Meikle 1984).

Salix aurita × ***repens (S.*** × ***ambigua)***   C 15,25

Plants of this hybrid can usually found by systematically searching areas where both parents grow and it is probably more widespread in eastern Coll than the existing records suggest: heathy rock outcrop above L. Ballyhaugh, 175578, DAP, CDP *et al.*, 1997; Meall nam Muc area, 25, HH; rocks near the sea SW of Arinagour, 2255, DAP, CDP *et al.*, 1997.

[***Salix aurita*** × ***viminalis (S.*** × ***fruticosa)***

Recorded by HH "in Central Coll", a surprisingly vague record which was presumably made at the only site where HH recorded *S. viminalis*, near Arinagour. Although this is a widespread but uncommon hybrid, confirmation of its occurrence on Coll is desirable, especially as *S. viminalis* is only present on the island as a planted shrub.]

[***Salix caprea***   Goat Willow

Recorded from several sites by TD (Dargie 1993), records which we take to be errors for *S. aurita* or *S. cinerea* which he did not record.]

Salix cinerea subsp. ***oleifolia***   Grey Willow   C 15,25,26

Much rarer than *S. aurita*, and confined to eastern Coll: Acha, 184547, BSB, 1988; woodland fragment on coast SW of Arinagour, 219556, DAP & CDP, 1997; in plantation, Gallanach, 219605, BSB, 1988; islands in L. Ghille-caluim ("exceptionally fine"), 26, HH.

[***Salix myrsinifolia***   Dark-leaved Willow

Recorded by HH (as *S. andersoniana*) from an island in L. Ghille-caluim, C 26. A 10km square record from 26, CDP & NFS, 1989, probably refers to the same site as the recorders noted "much *Salix*" on the two wooded islands in this lake. This species is predominantly eastern in Britain and very rare in NW Scotland (Stewart *et al.* 1994); it is not recorded from Mull. However, it is known from scattered cliffs and ravines in the Outer Hebrides and its presence on Coll is not impossible.]

Salix pentandra   Bay Willow   C 15,(25)

Recorded as a planted tree from near Arinagour and Breachacha by HH and more recently from E of Uig, 179544, CDP & NFS, 1989; Acha, 184548, CDP & NFS, 1990; village of Arinagour, 25, AW, 1986.

Salix repens   Creeping Willow   All except T 05

Frequent in coastal heaths and rocky moorlands, often with *Calluna vulgaris, Erica cinerea, Festuca rubra* and *Hydrocotyle vulgaris.*

Salix triandra   Almond Willow   C 15,26

Planted at Uig, 170547, BSB, 1988 and near Arnabost, 219602, BSB, 1988.

Salix viminalis   Osier   T 94,(04), C 15,25,26

This is now the most frequent of the willows planted as hedges or individually by habitations, although HH mentions it only near Arinagour.

Salsola kali subsp. *kali*   Prickly Saltwort   T (94),04; (G); C 15

A rare plant of strandlines, only recently recorded from Traigh Mhor, 054474 and 062475, TD, 1993; Port Ruadh, 084496, BSBI, 1990; Traigh Gharbh, 1353, DAP & CDP, 1997; SE of L. Breachacha, 1652, DAP & CDP, 1997. Described as "locally common" on Tiree by Macvicar (1898).

Sambucus nigra   Elder   T 93,94,(04); C 15,25,26

Scattered records, usually by or near houses, old and new, and almost certainly an introduction.

Samolus valerandi   Brookweed   All

Widespread and quite frequent in streams, pools, dune slacks, saltmarshes and damp tracks near the coast, and occurring inland in the calcareous marsh S of L. Riaghain, 034468, CDP & NFS, 1989.

Saxifraga hirsuta   Kidney Saxifrage   C (15)

Acha burn by road, 1854, JWC, 1983, det. AMcGS, **E.**

Saxifraga hypnoides   Mossy Saxifrage   C all

Frequent and well-recorded on dunes and sandy places from two limited areas: from around Traigh Hogh, 1656, and Machair Mhor, 1757; and from Cliad, 1960 and 2059, to Gallanach, 2167. Although *S. hypnoides* reaches the coast further north in Sutherland almost all the records in Mull and Skye are from wet rock faces at some altitude. The only record from the Outer Hebrides is from the summit of Beinn Mhor in South Uist.

The unexpected finding of this species on Coll is well described by Heslop Harrison (1939a).

Saxifraga tridactylites   Rue-leaved Saxifrage   T 94,04; C 15,26

Similarly on dunes, but more widespread.

[***Scabiosa columbaria***   Small Scabious

Reported from Ceann a'Mhara, 937397, TD (Dargie 1993). An obvious error.]

Schoenoplectus lacustris   Common Club-rush   C 15,25,26

Rare in lochs and ditches on Coll with only one site in 15, at L. Fada, 1958, CDP, 1990. There is a large stand in the centre of L. an t-Sagairt, 2560. The only Tiree record, from An Fhaodhail, 04, is probably an error for *S. tabernaemontani.* For a map of recent records, see Fig. 4.

Schoenoplectus tabernaemontani   Grey Club-rush   T 94,04; C 25

Scattered in some of the small saltmarshes on the north coast of Tiree and in the central valley of An Fhaodhail. It is also found in the interesting saline area to the NW of L. a'Phuill, 94, with *Blysmus rufus.* On Coll only recorded from L. Eatharna, 225581, SJL, 1990. There is a record for 26, from Gallanach, but this might relate to *S. lacustris* which is frequent there. For a map of recent records, see Fig. 9.

Schoenus nigricans   Black Bog-rush   T 93,94,04; G 05; C 15,25,26

Frequent in base-rich flushes with *Carex hostiana* and other sedges. Very much a plant of the western seaboard in Scotland. Found in 41 1km squares on Tiree.

Scilla verna   Spring Squill   T 93,94,04,(05); G 05,15; C 15,26

Quite widespread, but local, on rocky ledges and cliff-top turf on Tiree and Gunna. Rare on Coll, with records from: W side of Feall Bay, 130545, CG & AGP, 1999; near Port-na-Luing, 1552, BKC, 1997; top of Cornaig rock, 26, JWC, 1987; Dun Morbhaidh, 235635, PFB, 1987+; Traigh Tuath, 274639, PFB, 1987+.

Scrophularia nodosa   Common Figwort   T (04); C (25)

Recorded only by HH, from "rising ground east of Ruaig", 04, and a "ditch near Arinagour", 25. It is very odd that this has not been seen again, especially as it is frequent along the west coast, on Mull and on Skye.

Scutellaria galericulata   Skullcap   T 93,04; C 25,(26)

Very rare, with all the recent records coming from very close to the sea: near shore, Hynish, 93, LF & RS, 1988; in splash zone E of Millton, 095473, BSBI, 1990; NE of Arinagour, 25, BSBI, 1989.

Scutellaria minor   Lesser Skullcap   T (04); (G); C (15),25,26

Just as rare as the preceding, but on moorlands as well as by the shore: Caolas-an-eilean, 219556, DAP, CDP *et al.*, 1997; L. an Duin, 2157, CDP & NFS, 1989; L a'Mhill, 2560, CDP & NFS, 1989. Recorded from the coast of Tiree, SE of Millton, 092472, IC (Dargie 1993) but this may be an error for *S. galericulata* which was recorded by BSBI at 095473.

Sedum acre   Biting Stonecrop   T 93,94,04; (G); C 15,25,26

Frequent on machair and other sandy places.

[***Sedum album***   White Stonecrop

Around a radar station, Sandaig, 938430, TD; on eroding machair SW of Hynish, 976388, TD; on machair, Balephetrish, 010472, TD (all Dargie 1993). We have taken these as errors for *S. anglicum* or *S. acre.*]

Sedum anglicum   English Stonecrop   All

Frequent amongst rocks both on the coast, and in drier areas inland.

Sedum rosea   Roseroot   T 94; C 15,16,(25),26

On Tiree only found on sea cliffs at Ceann a'Mhara, most recently from the large north-facing cliff on the west side, 938411, DAP & CDP, 1997. Apparently frequent on sea cliffs on Coll (HH) but the only recent records are: Ben Feall, 143552 and 146552, DAP & CDP, 1997; N of Cliad, 1960, JWC, 1991; A'Chroic, 26G, JWC, 1988.

Selaginella selaginoides   Lesser Clubmoss   T 93,94,04; (G); C 15,(25),26

Quite widespread in machair and in basic flushes on moorlands.

Senecio aquaticus   Marsh Ragwort   All

Frequent and widespread in all wet habitats.

Senecio aquaticus × ***jacobaea (S.*** × ***ostenfeldii)***   T (04); C (25),26

Caoles, 04, BSBI, 1968, **BM**; near Arinagour, 25, HH; with parents, Dun Morbhaidh, 26, JWC, 1987, **E**.

Senecio jacobaea   Common Ragwort   All

Frequent and widespread in dunes, machair and ruderal situations.

[*Senecio sylvaticus*   Heath Groundsel

Recorded by HH from crags E of Machair Mhor, C 15. Very rare on the west coast of Scotland, but found on strandlines on Mull, and rarely on rocks and in a quarry on Skye. On balance the record seems unlikely.]

* *Senecio viscosus*   Sticky Groundsel   C 25

Four plants on the landing pier, Arinagour, 225562, DAP, CDP *et al.*, 1997.

Senecio vulgaris   Groundsel   T 93,94,04; (G); C 15,25,26

Widespread in gardens and waste places but also occurring on fore-dunes, a more natural habitat.

[*Seriphidium maritimum*   Sea Wormwood

T 04, IAW, det. AJW, without a date or location on the card sent to BRC. The specimen is purportedly in **BM**, but we have not found it. This is an unlikely species to occur as a native on Tiree, as it has not been recorded on the west coast of Britain north of Cumbria. In 1998 JWC commented that "with Clive Jermy I looked for this in '84 near shore but only plant was in a small garden nearby. A cutting has grown happily, and flowered, in my garden ever since".]

Sherardia arvensis   Field Madder   T 04; C (15),25,26

A rare weed of disturbed ground and sandy rock outcrops: N of Tiree Aerodrome, 002447, TD, 1993; seemingly persistent at Cliad, 206590, JWC, 1984, **E**, and DAP, CDP *et al.*, 1997; rock outcrop NW of Arnabost, 205603, JWC, 1987.

Silene dioica   Red Campion   T (93),94,(04)

Extremely rare in sea-gorges on Ceann a'Mhara, 94. Recorded here from Macvicar (1898) up to 1997, DAP & CDP. There are also old records from Hynish, 93, SMM, and from cliffs at An Cnap, 0449, HH.

?* *Silene latifolia*   White Campion   T 04; C (15),26

Not recorded by HH but reported a few times since from hayfields or field edges: Tiree Aerodrome, 002447, TD, 1993, with *Sherardia arvensis*; Gallanach, 216608, BKC & KAHC, 1988. Unknown on Mull, and occasional as an arable weed on Skye.

Silene uniflora   Sea Campion   T 93,94,04,(05); G 05,15; C 15,(25),26

Widespread on rocks, cliffs and sand dunes, but surprisingly local.

Sinapis arvensis   Charlock   T 93,94,04; C (15),(25),26

An weed of arable land, described as "everywhere in fields" by HH but declining with the habitat and now only occasional. Only once seen in 1997.

*Sisymbrium officinale   Hedge Mustard   T (93),94,04; C 25,26

Occasional as a weed in gardens and cultivated ground.

*Sisymbrium orientale   Eastern Rocket   T (04)

Garden weed in guest house at Baugh, BSBI, 1968.

[*Sisyrinchium bermudiana*   Blue-eyed-grass

Damp slope in SE angle of L. Cliad, C 25, HH only. The BSBI party searched for this species here in 1967, but the area was closely grazed by sheep and they failed to find it (Duncan 1968a,b).]

*Solanum tuberosum   Potato   T 04; C 26

Occasional as a weed on beaches: at the outlet of An Fhaodhail, 016439, TD, 1993; Vaul, 045485, IC, 1993. Also recorded from a dump at Cliad, 204600, JWC, 1987.

*Soleirolia soleirolii   Mind-your-own-business   C (15),25,26

First recorded by VG in 1960, from 15 and 25, and now naturalised in and outside several gardens on Coll.

Solidago virgaurea   Goldenrod   T (94); C 15,25,26

Not infrequent on rock ledges on Coll, but only recorded (by HH) from Beinn Hough on Tiree, a site searched without success by DAP, 1997.

Sonchus arvensis   Perennial Sow-thistle   T all; G 15; C 15,25,26

Occasional in coastal habitats, waste places or as a weed of cultivation.

Sonchus asper   Prickly Sow-thistle   T 93,94,04; (G); C all

More frequent than the preceding species in waste places and cultivated land.

Sonchus oleraceus   Smooth Sow-thistle   T 93,(94),(04); C 15,25,26

Rarely recorded from similar habitats to those of *S. asper*. Frequently recorded from Tiree by TD in 1993, but as he only recorded *S. arvensis* once, and the habitats of his records were more appropriate to that species, we have rejected these records.

[*Sorbus aria agg.*   Whitebeam

Recorded from Sorisdale area, 26, BSBI, 1967, but with no details or specimen. LG reports that the BSBI party "did a good deal of searching" for
HH's plants and that UKD "found his *Sorbus* still looking much the same."
There is, however, no reference to this species in HH and this presents a
mystery which remains to be solved.]

Sorbus aucuparia   Rowan   C 15,25,26

Uncommon but widespread on Coll in rocky gorges, and on islands in
lochs, where protected from grazing and fires.

Sparganium angustifolium   Floating Bur-reed   T 94,04; C 15,25,26

Widespread and frequent in lochs and streams. For a map of recent
records, see Fig. 8.

[*Sparganium emersum*   Unbranched Bur-reed

Recorded by HH and BSBI, 1968, from T 94, 04 and C 25, 26. We are
provisionally treating these records as errors for *S. angustifolium*, which
HH did not record and which is undoubtedly frequent on the islands.
However, populations such as that in a pool NW of L. Anlaimh, 185560,
NFS, 1990, **CGE**, are difficult to identify and there is a possibility that *S.
emersum* or its hybrid with *S. angustifolium* might be confirmed from the
islands.]

Sparganium erectum   Branched Bur-reed   T 94,04; C all

Frequent by coastal streams and ditches, and also found by the more base-
rich lochs and pools.

Sparganium natans   Least Bur-reed   T 94; C (15)

Very rare in lochans, with only two confirmed records: SW of L. Stanail,
968444, MGBH & CDP, 1990, **CGE**; L. Ballyhaugh, 15, BSBI, 1967,
DEE (searched for subsequently but not refound). Although it was reported
from at least seven other sites by TD (Dargie 1993) we have rejected these
records as errors for *S. angustifolium*, which he did not record.

Spergula arvensis   Corn Spurrey   T (94),04; C 15,25,26

Still quite frequent on cultivated ground, and found in gardens too.

Spergularia marina   Lesser Sea-spurrey   T 94,04; C 15,25

A rare plant of saltmarshes, recorded recently only by SJL in 1989 and
1990, in seven locations.

Spergularia media Greater Sea-spurrey T 94,04; C 15,25,26

Occasionally found in saltmarshes, but more frequent than *S. marina.*

* ***Spergularia rubra*** Sand Spurrey C (26)

Recorded only by HH as "very rare in one field east of Gallanach". On the west coast only recorded from Skye and Lewis, and marked in Murray (1980) and Pankhurst & Mullin (1991) as possibly introduced. It may have been a casual on Coll.

Spiranthes romanzoffiana Irish Lady's-tresses C all

This orchid grows in acidic, nutrient-poor, predominantly cattle-grazed vegetation on Coll. Its precise habitat requirements have recently been studied by Henderson (1996), who recorded the species with which it was associated in 110 1m^2 quadrats. *Carex panicea* and *Molinia caerulea* were almost constant associates, and the following occurred in over half the quadrats: *Anagallis tenella, Anthoxanthum odoratum, Carex echinata, C. nigra, Eriophorum angustifolium, Holcus lanatus, Hydrocotyle vulgaris, Juncus articulatus, Nardus stricta, Ranunculus flammula* and *Succisa pratensis.* Henderson showed that the vegetation in which *S. romanzoffiana* grows can be classified into four intergrading types: periodically flooded grassland with *Caltha palustris, Equisetum fluviatile* and *Potentilla palustris,* drier grassland with *Cynosurus cristatus* and *Nardus stricta,* heathier communities with *Calluna vulgaris, Erica tetralix* and *Sphagnum* spp. and base-enriched, slightly flushed sites with *Pinguicula vulgaris, Schoenus nigricans, Selaginella selaginoides* and the moss *Scorpidium scorpioides.* The first record of *S. romanzoffiana* on Coll was made by J. Heslop Harrison in 1939, on the northern shores of L. Cliad, 2059. Since then it has been recorded from about 30 sites, with three main concentrations; around Arileod and Uig, 15; in the Cliad area, 15, 16, 25; and in a few spots from Torastan to Eileraig, 26. There are outliers near Totamore, 15. *S. romanzoffiana* is a scarce plant in Britain, recorded from 20 10km squares and 53 1km squares from 1970 onwards. The Coll populations from 4 10km squares and 18 1km squares therefore represent a significant proportion of the British total.

Stachys arvensis Field Woundwort T 93; C 15,(26)

A very occasional weed of gardens and arable. Hynish, 9839, BSBI, 1990; Acha, 15, JWC, 1987.

Stachys palustris Marsh Woundwort T (93),94,04; C (15),25,26

A relatively rare plant of ditches. There are only four recent records, but three of these were made in a short visit in 1997, and it must be more frequent.

Stachys palustris × ***sylvatica (S.*** × ***ambigua)***   Hybrid Woundwort
C 15,25,26

Foot of wall, Garden House, Uig, 166542, DAP & CDP, 1997, **CGE**; wood, Arinagour, 219573, DAP, CDP *et al.*, 1997, **CGE**; W of Arnabost, 204600, JWC, 1988. HH describe it as "very common on Coll from Acha to Breachacha".

Stachys sylvatica   Hedge Woundwort   T 93,(94),(04); C 25

Macvicar (1898) and HH recorded this plant from rocky outcrops including Ceann a'Mhara, Ben Hynish, Beinn Hough and An Cnap on Tiree. The only recent record is from Hynish, 93, BSBI, 1990 and as a garden weed on Coll, 25.

*****Stellaria holostea***   Greater Stitchwort   C (25)

Recorded as a garden weed, Arinagour, JWC, 1983, and also previously from that area by HH and BSBI, 1967.

Stellaria media   Common Chickweed   All except C 16

Widespread as a weed in arable fields, gardens and waste places, and also occurring in nutrient-rich coastal habitats.

Stellaria uliginosa   Bog Stitchwort   T (93),94,04,05; G 05; C 15,25,26

Common in wet areas throughout the islands.

Suaeda maritima   Annual Sea-blite   T 94,04; C 15,(26)

Very local in saltmarshes. Recorded recently from a few sites on Tiree, and one on Coll: Caoles Mor, 126527, SJL, 1989.

Subularia aquatica   Awlwort   (C)

Recorded by HH as "very rare in Loch na Cloiche", but not reported since. It is quite widespread on Mull and Skye, and on the Ardnamurchan peninsula, so it is possible that they were correct. However, CDP and NFS have searched for it in vain in both L. na Cloiche W of Arinagour in C 25, which has a very peaty substrate and appears unsuitable, and L. na Cloiche in C 26.

Succisa pratensis   Devil's-bit Scabious   All

Very plentiful on wet moorlands. The dwarf var. *arenaria* occurs in species-rich coastal heath at Ceann a'Mhara, 9340, Ben Feall, 144551, and doubtless elsewhere.

*****Symphoricarpos albus***   Snowberry   C 25

Planted at The Lodge, Arinagour, DAP, CDP *et al.*, 1997.

*__Symphytum asperum__ × __officinale (S.__ × __uplandicum)__   Russian Comfrey
C (25)

Cliad Farm garden, JWC, 1986, **E**.

*__Tanacetum parthenium__   Feverfew   T 04,(05); C 25,26

An occasional garden weed.

*__Tanacetum vulgare__   Tansy   T 94,(04); C (25),(26)

A garden escape near habitations. It is odd that there have only been two records since HH, the latest from a roadside verge in Moss, 94, CDP & NFS, 1989.

__Taraxacum__   Dandelion

The genus *Taraxacum* is widespread on the islands in a wide range of open habitats, especially dunes and roadsides; there are recent records from all squares. JWC made a special effort to collect material on Coll for determination by C.C. Haworth or A.J. Richards, and the microspecies of this island are therefore relatively well known. There is less information on the dandelions of Tiree, although AMcGS and JWC have collected some specimens on the island, which were determined by the same authorities. There is no material from Gunna. We are grateful to Andrew Dudman for a summary of the records used to compile the maps in the BSBI Handbook (Dudman & Richards 1997); further details of most of these collections were entered by JWC on her card index and, for some records, on record cards sent to BRC. The section to which each species belongs is indicated after the name. The most interesting dandelions on the islands are the ecologically and geographically restricted species in Sections *Erythrosperma* and *Obliqua*, which are found on dunes and shallow soil over rocks, but the rarest species is *T. rubellum*, which is recorded by Dudman & Richards (1997) from only 6 10km squares in Britain, all in Scotland and two on Coll. Nomenclature follows Dudman & Richards (1997).

__Taraxacum arenastrum__ (Erythrosperma)   T (94)

Kilkenneth dunes, 9344, AMcGS, 1982.

__Taraxacum dahlstedii__ (Ruderalia)   C (15),(25)

In ruins of old mill, Acha, 1854, JWC, 1983, det. CCH; Arinagour, 25, JWC, 1983, det. CCH, **E**.

__Taraxacum degelii__ (Erythrosperma)   C 16

Sand dunes, 1960, JWC, 1992, **E**.

Taraxacum duplidentifrons (Celtica)   C (15)

Breachacha farmyard, 15, JWC, 1983, **E**.

Taraxacum euryphyllum (Naevosa)   C (26)

Dunes, Gallanach, 26, JWC, 1983.

Taraxacum faeroense (Spectabilia)   C (15),16,(25),26

Quite widespread on Coll. 15, JWC, 1984; rock cleft, 1960, JWC, 1992;
peaty shore near Arinagour, 25, JWC, 1983; dunes near Gallanach, 26,
JWC, 1983; marshy ground, Arnabost, 208606, JWC, 1987.

Taraxacum fulvicarpum (Celtica)   T (04), C (25)

Gott Bay, 0447, AMcGS, 1982; Salum Bay, 0648, AMcGS, 1982; roadside, Arinagour, 25, JWC, 1983, det. CCH, **E**.

Taraxacum fulvum (Erythrosperma)   C (15)

Dunes, Ballyhaugh, 1757, JWC, 1983, **E**.

Taraxacum hamatum (Hamata)   C (25)

Arinagour, 25, JWC, 1983.

Taraxacum haworthianum (Erythrosperma)   T (04),(05); C (15),(26)

Gott Bay, 0447, AMcGS, 1982; Salum Bay, 0648, AMcGS, 1982; Urvaig,
0750, AMcGS, 1982; 15, JWC, 1983; damp machair, Cornaigbeg, 26,
JWC, 1983.

Taraxacum insigne (Ruderalia) C (25)

Roadside, Arinagour, 25, JWC, 1983, **E**.

Taraxacum landmarkii (Celtica)   C (15)

Machair and dunes, Ballyhaugh, 15, JWC, 1983, **E**.

Taraxacum laticordatum (Ruderalia)   C 25

Garden, Craigdarroch, Arinagour, 222573, JWC, 1992, **E**.

Taraxacum luteum (Celtica)   C (15),26

Rock cranny near sea, Breachacha, 15, JWC, 1983, det. CCH, **E**; farmyard, Cornaigbeg, 26, JWC, 1983, **E**; 258640, JWC, 1992.

Taraxacum maculosum (Naevosa)   C (15),(26)

Stream bank, Ballyhaugh, 15, JWC, 1983; dunes near Gallanach, 26,
JWC, 1983.

Taraxacum nordstedtii (Celtica) C 15

Sand dunes, Port an t-Saoir, 148550, JWC, 1992.

Taraxacum obliquum (Obliqua) T (04); C (15),26

Dunes, Salum Bay, 065486, AMcGS, 1982, **E**; 15, JWC, 1983; sandy hummocks, Arnabost, 207602, JWC, 1987; dunes, Gallanach, 26, JWC, 1983, **E**.

* *Taraxacum pectinatiforme* (Ruderalia) C (26)

Cemetery on dunes near Torastan, 26, JWC, 1983, **E**.

Taraxacum platyglossum (Obliqua) C (15)

Machair, Crossapol Bay, 15, UKD, 1967, **BM**; Ballyhaugh dunes, 15, JWC, 1983, **E**.

Taraxacum polyodon (Ruderalia) C (25)

Arinagour, 25, JWC, 1983.

Taraxacum richardsianum (Naevosa) C (15)

15, JWC, 1983.

Taraxacum rubellum (Naevosa) C (15),(26)

Hogh Bay, 15, JWC, 1983, **E**; Gallanach dunes, 26, JWC, 1983.

Taraxacum subnaevosum (Naevosa) T (94),(04),(05); C 15,16,26

The Green, 9648, AMcGS, 1982; quarry, Balephetrish, 0147, JWC, 1984, det. CCH, **E**; Urvaig, 0750, AMcGS, 1982; rock crack near Gortan, 15, JWC, 1983; machair, Ballyhaugh, 15, JWC, 1983; 148550, JWC, 1992; sand dunes, 1960, JWC, 1992; Gallanach dunes, 26, JWC, 1983, **E**; 258640, JWC, 1992.

Taraxacum unguilobum (Celtica) C (15),16,(25),26

The commonest dandelion on Coll therefore details of the records were not retained on the BSBI card index. 15, JWC, 1983; 1960, JWC, 1992; 25, JWC, 1983; 26, JWC, 1983; field verge, Arnabost, 209602, JWC, 1987; 258640, JWC, 1992.

Teucrium scorodonia Wood Sage T 93,(94),(04); (G); C 15,25,26

On Tiree the only recent record is from Hynish, 93U, BSBI, 1990; it is surprising that it has not been seen on Ceann a'Mhara. Seemingly quite widespread and not infrequent on rock ledges and ravines on Coll.

Thalictrum minus   Lesser Meadow-rue   T 93,94,04; G 15; C 15,25,26
Plentiful on dunes and machair.

Thymus polytrichus   Wild Thyme   All
Common and widespread in all drier places, including rocks and sand
dunes. This species includes all four species reported by HH from the
islands. White-flowered plants which lack anthocyanin pigments in both
calyx and stem grow on dunes at the west end of Coll.

* ***Torilis japonica***   Upright Hedge-parsley   (G); C (25)
Recorded by HH from Gunna and Arinagour. There are odd records of
isolated plants in Mull and Skye, and HH's records may be correct, but
only as a casual.

Trichophorum cespitosum   Deergrass   All except T 05
Widespread in moorland throughout the islands.

[***Trifolium bocconei***   Twin-headed Clover
Recorded by HH from Caoles, C 15, but rejected for reasons explained
in the introduction.]

Trifolium campestre   Hop Trefoil   T 93,94,04; C 15,(25),26
Habitat unknown. Only recorded from one spot by HH, but quite frequently elsewhere up to the BSBI trip in 1967. Since then recorded at:
resown field, Hynish, 983393, TD, 1993; Traigh Bail'-a-mhuillinn, 9548,
BSBI, 1990; Baugh, 019442, TD, 1993; Ruaig, 063477, TD, 1993; W of
Breachacha, 15, DAP & CDP, 1997; Cornaigbeg, 242632, JWC, 1988, det.
TCGR. It is difficult to reconstruct the history of the species on the islands
from these inconsistent records although it may have been sown in
improved leys.

Trifolium dubium   Lesser Trefoil   T (93),(94),04; (G); C (15),25,26
Described as "locally very common" by Macvicar (1897a) and "common
enough everywhere" by HH, yet there are no recent records from several
10km squares.

Trifolium fragiferum   Strawberry Clover   C 15
Tall turf at edge of stream above beach at Port an t-Saoir, Ben Feall,
147548, CDP, 1997, **CGE**. This is the only record since HH who recorded
it from Caoles and to the W and N of Arileod, not far from Ben Feall. The
record was long doubted, if only because the nearest sites are at North
Berwick and in Cumbria, although there is a recent record from the Outer
Hebrides.

Trifolium medium   Zigzag Clover   T 93,94,(04); C all

Found on cliffs and in ruderal habitats; very rarely in turf. On Tiree the only recent records are from Ben Hynish and Ceann a'Mhara.

Trifolium pratense   Red Clover   All

Common in pastures, and on cliffs.

Trifolium repens   White Clover   All

Very common in most fertile habitats, including saltmarshes.

Triglochin maritimum   Sea Arrowgrass   T all; (G); C all

Common in saltmarshes and amongst rocks by the sea.

Triglochin palustre   Marsh Arrowgrass   All except G 05

Frequent in marshy and fenny places.

Tripleurospermum inodorum Scentless Mayweed T 94; G 15; C 25,26

An occasional weed of disturbed ground.

Tripleurospermum maritimum   Sea Mayweed   All

Widespread in shingle and amongst rocks near the sea.

[*Trisetum flavescens*   Yellow Oat-grass

Recorded on Tiree by HH, by Vose *et al.* (1957) and from the W side of The Reef, T 94, BSBI, 1968. Extremely rare in the west of Scotland, with no records from Mull, or from Ardnamurchan, dots in the *Atlas* from Eigg and Canna, and one record from Skye. Either a casual or a mistake.]

Tussilago farfara   Colt's-foot T 94,(04); G 15; C 15,(25),26

Locally abundant on foredunes, and occasionally found on waste ground.

[*Typha angustifolia*   Lesser Bulrush

Recorded at the N end of An Fhaodhail, 007463, TD, 1993. There are no other records from the Hebrides and we have not accepted this in the absence of confirmation, although it is a distinctive species. There is another record of *Typha* sp. from An Fhaodhail (see below).]

Typha latifolia   Bulrush   T (94)

Marshes W of Barrapol, 945427 and 949426, CJC, 1983. The presence of *T. latifolia* on Tiree is surprising, as there are no native records north of the Great Glen, but the species is spreading in Britain (Preston & Croft 1997). A record of *Typha* sp. from An Fhaodhail, 016446, PW, 1983, might also refer to this species.

*__Ulex europaeus__   Gorse   T 94,04; C 15,25,(26)

Noted by HH as "probably introduced". It was recorded in seven local-ities on Tiree by the BSBI in 1990, but always in discrete clumps.

__Urtica dioica__   Common Nettle   All except C 16

Widespread, particularly near houses or as a relic of farming.

__Urtica urens__   Small Nettle T (93),94,04,05; (G); C 15,25,26

Still frequent wherever crops are grown, and as a weed of beaches enriched by decaying seaweed.

__Utricularia intermedia sens. lat.__   Intermediate Bladderwort
                                                          T 93,94,04; C 15,25,26

In acidic swamps, flushes, ditches, small pools and the edge of lochs, where it often grows with _Potamogeton polygonifolius_, and as a lax aquatic form in the deeper water of lochs. Quite well distributed, but much more frequent in central and eastern Coll than elsewhere. The segregate _U. ochroleuca_ (Pale Bladderwort) has been recorded from L. a'Ghruibe, 258625, FH, 1991, det. PT. Two more records from Tiree have to be confirmed. For a map of recent records, see Fig. 5.

__Utricularia minor__   Lesser Bladderwort   T 93,94,04; C 15,25,26

In _Menyanthes_ swamps and peaty pools. Much more frequent in central and eastern Coll than elsewhere. Seen flowering in old peat diggings W of L. Anlaimh, 186558, and by lake N of L. Fada, 230596, in 1990. For a map of recent records, see Fig. 5.

__Utricularia vulgaris sens. lat.__   Bladderwort   T 94,04; C 15,25,26

In acidic marshes and lakes, and in highly calcareous habitats such as the pools S of L. Riaghain, 034468. Rare on Tiree, and less common than _U. intermedia_ and _U. minor_ on Coll.

__Vaccinium myrtillus__   Bilberry, Blaeberry   T (94); C (15),25,26

Uncommon in rocky places and ravines on moorlands. Recorded from Tiree only from the Barrapol area, BSBI, 1968, which seems a rather unlikely locality for this species. On Coll occasional, with only a few recent records.

__Valeriana officinalis__   Common Valerian   T (93),(94); C 15,(25)

The only recent records are from the burn below Uig down to Allt Mor, 1654, AW, 1984, and DAP & CDP, 1997.

Valerianella locusta   Common Cornsalad   T 94,(04); G; C all

Occasional on dunes. Recent records are from: Hough Bay, 94, BSBI, 1990; Totamore, 1656, LF, 1997; dunes near Cliad, 1960, JWC, 1991; Craigdarroch, Arinagour, 223573, BKC, 1998; dunes near Bousd, 255637, JWC, 1987.

* Verbascum thapsus   Great Mullein   C 15

A few plants growing as a garden weed W of Uig, 164542, DAP & CDP, 1997.

* Veronica agrestis   Green Field-speedwell   C (15),26

Cart ruts at Totronald, 169563, JWC, 1984, **E**; dump, Sorisdale, 26, JWC, 1988.

Veronica anagallis-aquatica   Blue Water-speedwell   T 93,94,04; C all

Common in streams, ditches, marshes and on poached mud, especially near the coast.

Veronica arvensis   Wall Speedwell   T 93,94,04,(05); (G); C all

Quite common in waste places and on fixed dunes.

Veronica beccabunga   Brooklime   T 94,04; C 15,25,26

Occasional in streams and similar habitats. For a map of recent records, see Fig. 9.

Veronica catenata   Pink Water-speedwell   C (15)

With *Baldellia ranunculoides, Ranunculus baudotii, R. trichophyllus* and *V. anagallis-aquatica*, Lochan a'Chuirn, 1152, AW, 1986, **E**. Elsewhere in the west of Scotland only found in the Outer Hebrides, with an old record from Islay.

Veronica chamaedrys   Germander Speedwell   T (04); C 15,25,26

On Tiree only ever found at Scarinish, where it was last recorded in 1959. On Coll quite frequent on dunes at Crossapol and from Arnabost to the north-east.

* Veronica filiformis   Slender Speedwell   T (04); C (15),25

Established in few places, but with only one recent record: hotel, Arinagour, 25, JWC, 1987.

[*Veronica montana* Wood Speedwell

Only recorded by HH, as "rare at the base of rocks near Sorisdale", C 26. There are a few other scattered records in western Scotland, almost entirely from woods.]

Veronica officinalis Heath Speedwell T 93,(94),04; (G); C all

Fairly rare, chiefly on dry rock ledges.

* *Veronica persica* Common Field-speedwell T 93,94,(04); C 25,26

A rarely recorded weed. Macvicar (1898) found a few plants about the Hotel grounds on Tiree but the species was not recorded by HH and there are only five recent records: walled garden, Hynish, 93, JWC, 1990; Mannal, 9840, BSBI, 1990; Cliad, 2059, DAP, CDP *et al.*, 1997; Achamore, 214596, DAP & CDP, 1997; Gallanach, 213608, JWC, 1988.

* *Veronica polita* Grey Field-speedwell T (04)

Recorded only by HH as "in fields near Kirkapoll and as a garden weed near Baugh".

Veronica scutellata Marsh Speedwell T 94,04; C 15,(25),26

Fairly common and quite widespread in marshes on moorlands and by lochs.

Veronica serpyllifolia Thyme-leaved Speedwell
T (93),(94),04; C (15),25,26

Rare on Tiree, with only one recent record: An Traigh-lochain, 0849, BSBI, 1990. Quite well distributed in wet turf on Coll.

Vicia cracca Tufted Vetch All except T 05

Common on machair and occasionally found in other sandy habitats.

Vicia sativa subsp. *nigra* Narrow-leaved Vetch T (04); C 15,16,(26)

Recorded from sand dunes, with only two recent records: dunes W of Breachacha Castle, 1454, CG & AGP, 1999; Cliad, 1960, JWC, 1991.

* *Vicia sativa* subsp. *sativa* Common Vetch T (04); C (25),(26)

Recorded occasionally as a casual, but not since 1967.

Vicia sepium Bush Vetch T (93),94,04; G 15; C all

Scattered in many habitats, including rocks, dunes and cultivated ground. A dwarf variant was noted by Macvicar (1897a) and HH, and this taxon has recently been named var. *hartii* by Akeroyd (1996). There are recent records from Crossapol dunes, 15, KAHC and JWC & HJN, 1987, and from dunes N of Arnabost burn, 26, JWC, 1987, det. JRA, **E**.

Viola arvensis   Field Pansy   T 04; C 26

An arable weed, very rarely recorded: Ruaig, 065480, IC, 1993 and 070477, DAP & CDP, 1997; Dun Morbhaidh area, 26G, JWC, 1987.

Viola canina   Heath Dog-violet   T (04); C 15,(25)

Heslop Harrison (1939a) stated that this violet was "thinly dispersed throughout the island, but seemingly preferring the dunes". In the flora HH described it as "not uncommon locally on machair and moorland", with a list of localities, but it has only been recorded three times since: Crossapol, 15, BSBI, 1967, **BM**; Machair Mhor, 1756, AW, 1984, conf. DMM, **E**, and BKC, 1998.

[***Viola kitaibeliana***   Dwarf Pansy

Erroneously mapped on Tiree in Wigginton (1999).]

Viola palustris   Marsh Violet   T 94,(04); C 15,25,26

Rare in fens, usually with *Sphagnum*. The only recent record for Tiree is S of L. Stanail, 970445, NFS, 1990. On Coll it is local but more frequent, particularly in the centre and north-east.

[***Viola reichenbachiana***   Early Dog-violet

Only recorded by HH, from Balephetrish, T 04, and in two places on Coll, C 25. Barely recorded elsewhere in Scotland, and presumably an error for *V. riviniana*.]

Viola riviniana   Common Dog-violet   All

Common on moorlands and cliffs and occasionally found on machair.

Viola tricolor subsp. ***curtisii***   Wild Pansy   T (04); (G); C 15,26

Macvicar (1898) described this as occurring on Tiree "in abundance at Ruaig in a sandy pasture which extends nearly across the island", 04, and it was also recorded in this area by HH, but there are very few recent records other than from the dunes at Crossapol, 15.

Viola tricolor subsp. ***tricolor***   Wild Pansy   C (26)

An occasional arable weed, not found recently.

[*Vulpia bromoides*   Squirreltail Fescue

Only recorded by HH from a ditch between Acha and Uig, C 15. There are scattered records from western Scotland, but a ditch seems an odd habitat.]

[*Zannichellia palustris*   Horned Pondweed

Recorded from Tiree by TD (Dargie 1993). There are no specimens, and one record was from pools on a rocky headland north of Balephetrish, 016482, a habitat which suggests *Ruppia maritima*. We have excluded it for these reasons. Recorded by HH from a stream near Gallanach, C 26, but never confirmed. The species is very rare in western Scotland, other than on the west side of the Outer Hebrides.]

Zostera marina   Eelgrass   T (94),04; C 15,25,26

Occasional records, often only of strandline plants, from many beaches. We know of no records of populations *in situ.*

[*Zostera noltei*   Dwarf Eelgrass

Recorded by HH as "washed ashore on Crossapol Bay", C 15, but even if correct, there is no reason to suggest it was of local origin.]

Tiree Cyperaceae

by D. A. Pearman

A week's holiday in June 1990 presented the opportunity to survey a whole island on a detailed (1km square) basis. With a certain amount of assistance every square was visited except four squares around Ben Hynish and two more which largely comprise the airfield. Records from later visits have been incorporated for these six squares. The other 118 squares or part squares were all visited once, with the exception of the richer areas which were covered twice.

In all just over 1150 records were made covering 35 species. The number of different species found in each 10km square is shown as Fig. 11. In addition special searches were made for species which were recorded by Heslop Harrison and others but not seen since. The distribution of the commoner species is shown as Figs 12–15. These are based on all recent records localised to 1km squares.

A week's survey work by an amateur is no basis for an ecological survey of a diverse island. The following notes may assist the interpretation of the distribution maps but do not pretend to be exhaustive.

Habitats

Upland and unimproved moorland

These areas are mainly sliabh (wet acid peat with a pH of 4.0–4.5 (Wormell 1989)), with the expected characteristic species such as *Eriophorum angustifolium*, *Carex nigra*, *C. panicea* and *C. echinata*. However, there were frequent flushes with a higher pH where *C. hostiana*, *C. dioica* and *C. pulicaris* were common together with *Eleocharis quinqueflora* and *Schoenus nigricans*. These were such constant associates that where one found one species it was worth searching for the others.

Lochs and their surrounds

Shepherd (1989) suggests that all bodies of standing open water are close to neutral (pH 7.0) despite the acid nature of surrounding peat-base substrate and vegetation, very probably due to the high levels of electrolytes from sea-spray and rain. Most of the lochs were fairly poor in vegetation. *C. rostrata* was only occasional and it was only where these lochs were reverting to fen that any substantial number of species were recorded – such as the little lochan to the west of Dun Beag at NM0749, where *C. diandra* was scattered with at least eight other species.

It was the surrounds of the lochs that were exciting, particularly the slightly barer areas (less competition?). Here, after only a day in the field, one could identify an area as being suitable for *C. viridula* subsp. *brachyrrhyncha* and *C. viridula* subsp. *viridula* and know it would be so. This was true of most of the larger lochs and stream systems, particularly An Fhaodhail (0145 etc.) and the lochs to the east, L. a'Phuill (9542), L. Stanail (9745) and L. Riaghain (0346) etc.

In addition there were two lochside sites where coastal species were found: Barrapol (9442) where *Blysmus rufus* and *Schoenoplectus tabernaemontani* were in fair quantity with *C. viridula* subsp. *brachyrrhyncha* abundant, and the NW shore of L. Bhasapol (9647), where *B. rufus* was found again with *Eleocharis uniglumis* and *E. quinqueflora*, *Samolus valerandi*, *Triglochin maritimum* and *Oenanthe lachenalii*.

Improved fields

On the deeper rich soils where the machair meets the peat there was more improved pasture and consequently few species. This is well shown in the west of the island and in the north-east too, as well as to the west of the airport.

However, many fields had been improved in the past and have reverted. Boyd & Boyd (1990) quote Tiree as having a population of 4453 in 1831 and 760 in 1981, so there is now less pressure. Such land is characterised by *Juncus* spp., *Iris pseudacorus*, *Ranunculus acris*, *Rumex acetosa*, *Holcus lanatus*, *Trifolium repens* and *T. pratensis*, *Lychnis flos-cuculi*, *Caltha palustris*, *Dactylorhiza fuchsii* and not much else. Cyperaceae are limited to *Carex ovalis*, *C. echinata* and *C. nigra*, with *Eriophorum angustifolium* and *Eleocharis palustris*. There seemed to be no taller *Carex* species in the ditches at all.

Machair and coastal

The extensive areas of machair only support *C. arenaria* and *C. flacca*, although there is a small population of *C. caryophyllea* on sand-covered rocks in the far south-west (9340).

The coast has many discrete colonies of *C. distans* and *C. otrubae*. The north and east coasts particularly have small patches of saltmarsh, with *Bolboschoenus maritimus*, *Blysmus rufus*, *Eleocharis uniglumis* and three sites for *C. extensa*.

Acknowledgements

I am extremely grateful to Simon Leach for his many coastal records and enthusiasm, and to Chris Preston and Nick Stewart for encouragement (and for persuading me to start on this project instead of having a nice relaxing holiday). I am grateful too for the help of all the other BSBI members in the week, particularly to Agnes Walker for organising the whole event.

Figure 11

The number of species of Cyperaceae found in each 1km square on Tiree. The map is based on recent records (1987 onwards).

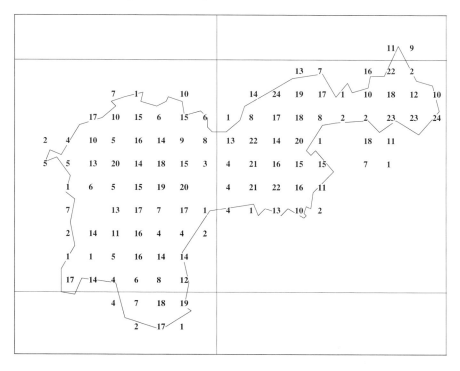

Figure 12

The distribution of some species of Cyperaceae on Tiree (1). The map is based on recent records (1987 onwards).

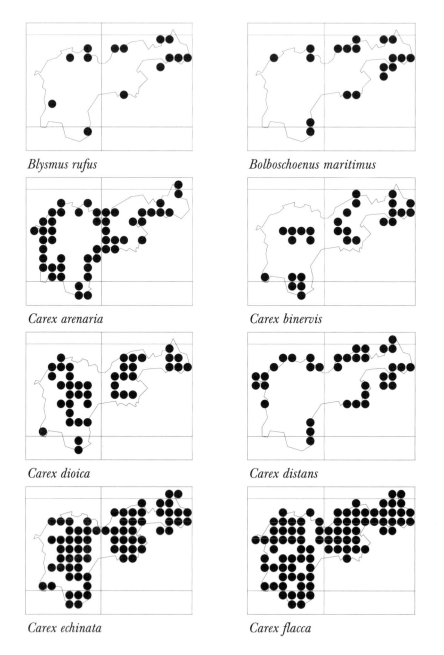

Blysmus rufus

Bolboschoenus maritimus

Carex arenaria

Carex binervis

Carex dioica

Carex distans

Carex echinata

Carex flacca

150

Figure 13

The distribution of some species of Cyperaceae on Tiree (2). The map is based on recent records (1987 onwards).

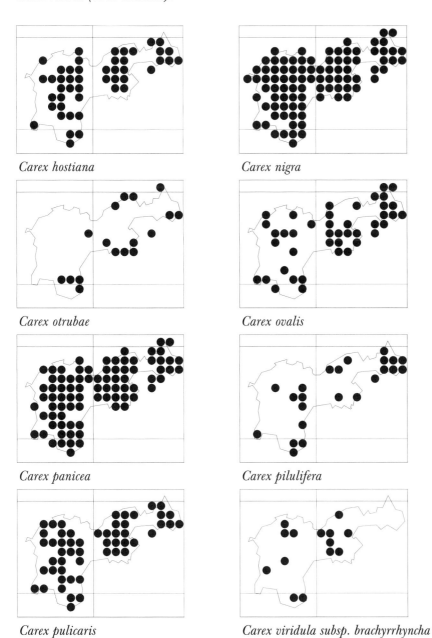

Carex hostiana

Carex nigra

Carex otrubae

Carex ovalis

Carex panicea

Carex pilulifera

Carex pulicaris

Carex viridula subsp. brachyrrhyncha

Figure 14

The distribution of some species of Cyperaceae on Tiree (3). The map is based on recent records (1987 onwards).

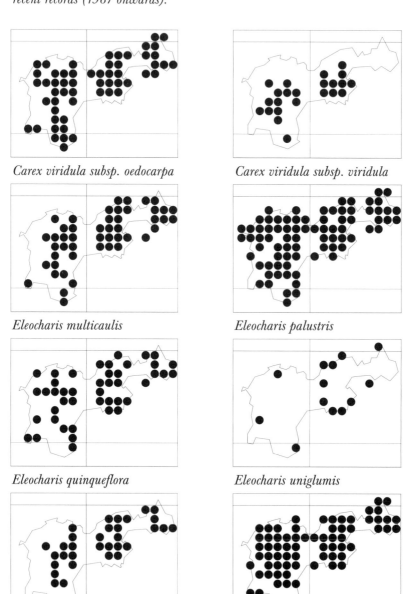

Carex viridula subsp. oedocarpa   Carex viridula subsp. viridula

Eleocharis multicaulis   Eleocharis palustris

Eleocharis quinqueflora   Eleocharis uniglumis

Eleogiton fluitans   Eriophorum angustifolium

Figure 15

The distribution of some species of Cyperaceae on Tiree (4). The map is based on recent records (1987 onwards).

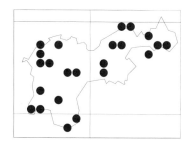

Isolepis setacea

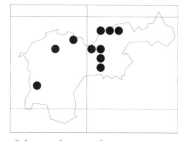

Schoenoplectus tabernaemontani

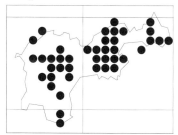

Schoenus nigricans

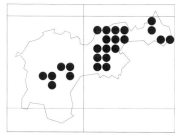

Trichophorum cespitosum

Stoneworts

by N.F. Stewart

The stonewort flora of Tiree and Coll has not previously been well studied. The main historical information comes from Macvicar's visits in 1896 and 1897 (Macvicar 1898, Groves & Groves 1898). He recorded eight species from Tiree and three from Coll, although two of the former were possibly errors (see below). Over the next ninety years there were only a few records; by I. A. Williams in 1947 (Tiree), C. W. Muirhead in 1951 (Coll) and J. W. Clark and A. C. Jermy in 1984 (Tiree). (There are specimens from these visits at the Natural History Museum and field records at the Biological Records Centre). This paucity of records is typical of many of the Hebridean islands although the publication of an identification handbook (Moore 1986) and a Red Data Book (Stewart & Church 1992) has contributed to a growing interest in the stonewort flora of these islands.

In 1989 and 1990, in connection with Botanical Society of the British Isles field meetings to the islands, the author with C. D. Preston visited over 300 water bodies on the two islands to investigate the aquatic flora. We found stoneworts in approximately a third of these and compiled over 230 records, most of which are backed by vouchers held at the South London Botanical Institute (**SLBI**). These show that this is one of the richest areas for stoneworts in Britain (Stewart 1996). A total of nine species have now been recorded from the two islands, eight on Tiree and seven on Coll and including four species that are nationally scarce. Gunna was also investigated in 1990 but no water bodies suitable for stoneworts were found. A more detailed account of the stoneworts of Tiree and Coll has been prepared for publication elsewhere (Stewart & Preston in press).

All records are by NFS and CDP unless otherwise stated. Abbreviations for other recorders are the same as those used for the vascular plant account.

Chara aspera   Rough Stonewort   T 94,04; C 15,25,26

> This is predominantly a plant of calcareous substrates in lakes and pools. Frequent on Tiree where it is known from 20 water bodies but absent from the Caoles peninsula. On Coll it is restricted to about five sites.

Chara contraria   Opposite Stonewort   T 94,04

> This is a species of calcareous sandy or marly substrates. Rare and restricted to the more calcareous parts of Tiree: L. Bhasapol, 94, SMM, 1897, and IAW, 1947; S side L. a'Phuill, 955412, 1990; An Fhaodhail, 018444 and

014458, 1990; L. Riaghain, 033468, SNHLS, 1994; loch N of L. Ghrianal, 038481, 1990. Both var. *contraria* and var. *hispidula* occur.

[*Chara globularis*   Fragile Stonewort

Macvicar (1898) recorded this species (under the name *C. fragilis*) as common on Scarinish Moor, Tiree, 04H, in 1896 but it is unlikely that the record is correct. *Chara virgata* is frequent in the Scarinish Moor area and it is much more likely that this is the plant that SMM saw.]

Chara hispida   Bristly Stonewort   T 94,04; C 15

An uncommon species of calcareous pools and lochs which is largely restricted to the machair but also occurs in cliff-top pools affected by salt-spray. Macvicar's (1898) records from Tiree are doubtful but the species has been recorded from several sites by later observers: L. Bhasapol, 968466, 1990; L. Earblaig, 9446, MARK, 1990; An Fhaodhail, 014458 and 0146, 1990; W of L. Dubh a'Gharraidh Fail, 0248, 1990; L. Riaghain, 034468, 1990; loch N of L. Ghrianal, 038481, 1990. On Coll it is restricted to the south-west: near Calgary Point, 109526, 1989; Lochan Seileach, 119517, 1989; between Ben Feall and Carpach, 151543, 1989.

Chara virgata   Delicate Stonewort   T 93,94,04; C 15,25,26

This species grows in a wide range of lakes, pools, streams and flushes. It is more tolerant of acid conditions than other *Chara* species. It is frequent on Tiree where it has been recorded from over 35 water bodies. On Coll it is frequent on the Caoles peninsula and within 1.5 kilometres of the north-west coast where it has been recorded from 15 sites. However, it is rare in the interior and south side of the island.

Chara vulgaris   Common Stonewort   T 93,94,04; C 15,26

This is mainly a plant of pools, streams and flushes. There are a few sites in larger lochs but here it is restricted to sheltered inlets, amongst emergent vegetation or in streams and flushes feeding into the lochs. It is occasional on Tiree where it occurs in 12 sites. On Coll it is restricted to the Caoles peninsula and to sandy areas along the north-west coast where it is occasional and recorded from 10 sites. Vars *vulgaris, longibracteata* and *papillata* have been recorded although var. *longibracteata* only from Tiree.

Nitella confervacea   Least Stonewort   C 26

A very rare plant of acid conditions with some organic component to the substrate. Known from only two sites in NE Coll: L. a'Mhill Aird, 230609, 1990, and L. a'Mhill Aird Bhig, 233604, 1990, and only in small quantity in both cases. It is the smallest of the stoneworts, reaching only 5cm tall and may have been overlooked in other sites in this area.

Nitella flexilis agg.   Smooth/Dark Stonewort   T (93),94,04; C all

This stonewort occurs in quite a variety of situations but it is usually in acid water bodies and avoids the sites surrounded by calcareous sand. It is frequent on Tiree where it has been recorded from 28 widely scattered sites. On Coll it is occasional and recorded from 10 sites, mostly close to the north-western coast. All fertile material which has been examined critically is *N. opaca* (Dark Stonewort), which is known from T 94,04; C 15,16,26 and may be the only segregate present.

Nitella translucens   Translucent Stonewort   T 93,94,04; C 15,25,26

This species is restricted to acid water bodies in the rockier parts of both islands. It is most frequent on the eastern peninsula of Tiree where it occurs in 15 water bodies. There are another eight sites between L. Bhasapol and Heylipol in W Tiree and four more to the south in the area SW of Balinoe. There are another eight sites scattered in the rockier parts of the island making a total of 35 sites. However, it was not refound at L. na Gile, 0248, where it was recorded by Macvicar (1898) but it still occurs in several places nearby. On Coll it occurs in 12 sites scattered through the central and eastern parts but it has not been refound at L. an Duin, 2157, where it was recorded by C.W. Muirhead in 1951.

Tolypella glomerata   Clustered Stonewort   T 94,04

This species is similar in ecology to *Chara contraria* with which it is associated at both sites. It grows in shallow water on calcareous sand or marl in places that probably dry out in dry summers. It has not previously been recorded from our area, where it occurs on the south side of L. a' Phuill 955412, 1990, and in several places along An Fhaodhail, 014458 and 017444, 1990.

ACKNOWLEDGEMENTS

Our main thanks must go to Mrs Joan Clark who did so much recording on the islands and who set up the card index on which our work is based. She commented on a draft of this Flora and we are very sorry that she did not live to see the published work. Our other main source of help was Dr Agnes Walker, who carried on Joan's work and organised the very successful BSBI visits of 1989 and 1990. We also thank the other participants on these meetings, especially Nick Stewart for his help with the recording of aquatic plants and for compiling the charophyte records and Simon Leach for recording salt-marsh species. We are grateful to the other botanists who have also made their records available to us, including Mrs P. Braithwaite, Dr C. J. Cadbury, Mrs B. Cassels, Dr T. Dargie, Miss C. Geddes, Ms S. Henderson, Dr O. Lassière (SNH Loch Survey) and Ms V. Morgan, and to the experts who have determined our specimens. P. D. Sell has been particularly helpful in allocating the specimens we have collected to the infraspecific taxa which will be recognised in the Flora he is writing with J. G. Murrell. Dr Larch Garrad sent us an entertaining and informative account of the 1967 BSBI Field Meeting and Douglas McKean facilitated access to herbarium material in Edinburgh. We are grateful to Lynne Farrell for the extended loan of the vice-county recorder's card index, for writing the foreword and for contributing the section on conservation. We thank colleagues at the Biological Records Centre for processing all the records, especially Henry Arnold for generating the distribution maps using the DMAP program written by Dr Alan Morton. Julie Gaunt kindly produced the other figures, Alison Stewart typed the bulk of the text and Bill Meek helped with the final editing. James Cadbury, Lynne Farrell and David McCosh provided valuable comments on a draft of the Flora and Gwynn Ellis prepared the index. Ian Boyd kindly gave us permission to modify maps in Boyd & Boyd (1990) for our Flora. The publication of this book was assisted by grants from the Professor Lloyd-Binn's bequest of the Glasgow Natural History Society and from Scottish Natural Heritage.

BIBLIOGRAPHY

Only works cited in the text are included in this bibliography. For an invaluable list of publications on the flora and vegetation of the Inner Hebrides, see Currie & Murray (1983).

Akeroyd, J.R. (1996). Coastal ecotypic variants of two vetches, *Vicia sepium* L. and *V. sylvatica* L. (Fabaceae), in Britain and Ireland. *Watsonia* **21**: 71–78.

Bennett, K.D., Bunting, M.J. & Fossitt, J.A. (1997). Long-term vegetation change in the Western and Northern Isles, Scotland. *Botanical Journal of Scotland* **49**: 127–140.

Bennett, K.D., Fossitt, J.A., Sharp, M.J. & Switsur, V.R. (1990). Holocene vegetational and environmental history at Loch Lang, South Uist, Western Isles, Scotland. *New Phytologist* **114**: 281–298.

Birks, H.J.B. & Williams, W. (1983). Late-Quaternary vegetational history of the Inner Hebrides. *Proceedings of the Royal Society of Edinburgh* **83B**: 269–292.

Boswell, J. (1785). *The journal of a tour to the Hebrides, with Samuel Johnson, Ll.D.* London.

Boyd, J.M. & Boyd, I.L. (1990). *The Hebrides.* Collins, London.

Cadbury, J. (1996). *Survey of the vegetation of the RSPB's Reef reserve, Tiree 1995.* Unpublished report, Royal Society for the Protection of Birds, Sandy.

Cadbury, J. & Cowie, N. (1998). *Machair vegetation monitoring on the Reef, Tiree, 1998.* Unpublished report, Royal Society for the Protection of Birds, Sandy.

Currie, A. & Murray, C.W. (1983). Flora and vegetation of the Inner Hebrides. *Proceedings of the Royal Society of Edinburgh* **83B**: 293–318.

Dargie, T. (1993). *Botanical survey of Tiree 1993. Survey methods and results.* Unpublished report to Scottish Natural Heritage.

Darling, F. Fraser (1955). *West Highland survey.* Oxford University Press, London.

Dudman, A.A. & Richards, A.J. (1997). *Dandelions of Great Britain and Ireland.* BSBI Handbook no. 9. Botanical Society of the British Isles, London.

Duncan, U.K. (1968a). Field meetings, 1967. Isle of Coll. 21st to 28th June. *Proceedings of the Botanical Society of the British Isles* **7**: 298–299.

Duncan, U.K. (1968b). Field meetings, 1967. Isle of Coll – 21st June–28th June. *Transactions of the Botanical Society of Edinburgh* **40**: 482–485.

Duncan, U.K. (1969). Field meetings, 1968. Isle of Tiree. 3rd–10th July. *Proceedings of the Botanical Society of the British Isles* **7**: 636–637. See also correction in *Watsonia* **8**: 194 (1970).

Duncan, U.K. (1970). Field meetings, 1968. Isle of Tiree – 3rd–10th July 1968. *Transactions of the Botanical Society of Edinburgh* **40**: 653–655.

Edees, E.S. & Newton, A. (1988). *Brambles of the British Isles.* Ray Society, London.

Farrell, L. (1983). *The status of* Eriocaulon aquaticum *in western Scotland.* Unpublished report, Nature Conservancy Council, South West (Scotland) region.

Fossitt, J.A. (1996). Late Quaternary vegetation history of the Western Isles of Scotland. *New Phytologist* **132**: 171–196.

Graham, G.G. & Primavesi, A.L. (1993). *Roses of Great Britain and Ireland.* BSBI Handbook no. 7. Botanical Society of the British Isles, London.

Green, F.H.W. & Harding, R.J. (1983). Climate of the Inner Hebrides. *Proceedings of the Royal Society of Edinburgh* **83B**: 121–140.

Groves, H. & Groves, J. (1898). Notes on British Characeae, 1895–1898. *Journal of Botany* **36**: 409–413.

Harrison, D.M. (1989). Agriculture and machairs on Tiree and Coll: a summary. In Stroud, D.A., ed. *Birds on Coll and Tiree: status, habitats and conservation,* pp. 19–24. Nature Conservancy Council & Scottish Ornithologists' Club, Edinburgh.

Henderson, S. (1996). *An investigation of the habitats of the scarce orchid, Spiranthes romanzoffiana Cham., on the Isle of Coll, Scotland.* M.Sc. thesis, Department of Botany, University of Reading.

Heslop Harrison, J. (1949). Field studies in *Orchis* L. I. The structure of dactylorchid populations on certain islands in the Inner and Outer Hebrides. *Transactions of the Botanical Society of Edinburgh* **35**: 26–66.

Heslop-Harrison, J. (1968). Genetic system and ecological habit as factors in dactylorchid variation. *Jahresberichte des Naturwissenschaftlichen Vereins in Wuppertal* **21/22**: 20–27.

Heslop Harrison, J.W. (1939a). A visit to the Isle of Coll. *Vasculum* **25**: 77–82.

Heslop Harrison, J.W. (1939b). The Hebridean form of the spotted orchid, *Orchis fuchsii* Druce. *Vasculum* **25**: 109–112.

Heslop Harrison, J.W. (1939c). Fauna and flora of the Inner and Outer Hebrides. King's College (University of Durham) Biological Expeditions. *Nature* **143**: 1004–1007.

Heslop Harrison, J.W. (1941a). Flora and fauna of the Inner and Outer Hebrides. *Nature* **147**: 134–136.

Heslop Harrison, J.W., ed. (1941b). A preliminary flora of the Outer Hebrides. *Proceedings of the University of Durham Philosophical Society* **10**: 228–273.

Heslop Harrison, J.W. (1949). Potamogetons in the Scottish Western Isles, with some remarks in the general natural history of the species. *Transactions of the Botanical Society of Edinburgh* **35**: 1–25.

Heslop Harrison, J.W. & Bolton, E. (1938). The rose flora of the Inner and Outer Hebrides and of other Scottish islands. *Transactions of the Botanical Society of Edinburgh* **32**: 424–431.

Heslop Harrison, J.W., Heslop Harrison, H., Clark, W.A. & Cooke, R.B. (1941). The flora of the Isles of Coll, Tiree and Gunna (v.-c. 110B). *Proceedings of the University of Durham Philosophical Society* **10**: 274–308.

Hollingsworth, P.M., Preston, C.D. & Gornall, R.J. (1996). Isozyme evidence for the parentage and multiple origin of *Potamogeton* × *suecicus* (*P. pectinatus* × *P. filiformis,* Potamogetonaceae). *Plant Systematics and Evolution* **202**: 219–232.

Horwood, A.R. & Noel, C.W.F. (1933). *The Flora of Leicestershire and Rutland.* Oxford University Press, London.

Hudson, G. & Henderson, D.J. (1983). Soils of the Inner Hebrides. *Proceedings of the Royal Society of Edinburgh* **83B**: 107–119.

Jermy, A.C. & Crabbe, J.A., eds (1978). *The island of Mull: a survey of its flora and environment.* British Museum (Natural History), London.

Johnson, S. (1775). *A journey to the Western Islands of Scotland.* London.

Kent, D.H. (1992). *List of vascular plants of the British Isles.* Botanical Society of the British Isles, London.

Kent, D.H. & Allen, D.E. (1984). *British and Irish herbaria.* Botanical Society of the British Isles, London.

Lascelles, M., ed. (1971). *A journey to the Western Islands of Scotland.* The Yale edition of the works of Samuel Johnson, **9**. Yale University Press, New Haven & London.

Leach, S.J. (in press). The saltmarshes of Coll and Tiree. *Botanical Journal of Scotland* **52**.

MacCulloch, J. (1819). *A description of the Western Islands of Scotland, including the Isle of Man.* 3 vols. Archibald Constable & Co., Edinburgh and Hurst, Robinson, & Co., London.

MacCulloch, J. (1824). *The Highlands and Western Isles of Scotland.* 4 vols. Longman, Hurst, Rees, Orme, Brown and Green, London.

Macdonald, J. (1811). *General view of the agriculture of the Hebrides, or Western Isles of Scotland.* Edinburgh.

McKay, M.M., ed. (1980). *The Rev. Dr. John Walker's Report on the Hebrides of 1764 and 1771.* John Donald Publishers, Edinburgh.

Macvicar, S.M. (1896). On the occurrence of *Eriocaulon* in Coll. *The Annals of Scottish Natural History* **1896**: 249–250.

Macvicar, S.M. (1897a). Plants of Tiree and Coll. *Journal of Botany* **35**: 54–57.

Macvicar, S.M. (1897b). On some Coll and Tiree plants. *Transactions of the Natural History Society of Glasgow* new series **5**: 55–57.

Macvicar, S.M. (1897c). *Eriocaulon* in Coll. *The Annals of Scottish Natural History* **1897**: 259.

Macvicar, S.M. (1898). On the flora of Tiree. *The Annals of Scottish Natural History* **1898**: 31–38, 81–97.

Madders, M. & Moser, M. (1989). Coastal waders in winter on Tiree and Coll. In Stroud, D.A., ed. *Birds on Coll and Tiree: status, habitats and conservation,* pp. 67–73. Nature Conservancy Council & Scottish Ornithologists' Club, Edinburgh.

Martin, M. (1703). *A description of the Western Islands of Scotland.* London. [Erroneously dated 1673 on title page.]

Mather, A.S., Smith, J.S. & Ritchie, W. (1975). *Beaches of northern Inner Hebrides.* Department of Geography, University of Aberdeen.

Meikle, R.D. (1984). *Willows and poplars of Great Britain and Ireland.* BSBI Handbook no. 4. Botanical Society of the British Isles, London.

Moore, J.A. (1986). *Charophytes of Great Britain and Ireland.* BSBI Handbook no. 5. Botanical Society of the British Isles, London.

Muirhead, C.W. (1952). Distributor's report for 1951. *Botanical Society of the British Isles Year Book* **1952**: 103–110.

Murray, W.H. (1973). *The Islands of Western Scotland. The Inner and Outer Hebrides.* Eyre Methuen, London.

Murray, C.W. (1980). *The botanist in Skye*, ed. 2. Botanical Society of the British Isles.

Palmer, M.A. & Bratton, J.H., eds (1995). *A sample survey of the flora of Britain and Ireland.* UK Nature Conservation no. 8. Joint Nature Conservation Committee, Peterborough.

Pankhurst, R.J. & Mullin, J.M. (1991). *Flora of the Outer Hebrides.* Natural History Museum Publications, London.

Parsons, M. (1984). *A provisional national review of the status of British micro-lepidoptera.* Unpublished report of the Nature Conservancy (NCC ISR 53).

Perring, F.H. & Sell, P.D. eds (1968). *Critical supplement to the Atlas of the British Flora.* Thomas Nelson & Sons, London.

Perring, F.H. & Walters, S.M. eds (1962). *Atlas of the British Flora.* Thomas Nelson & Sons, London.

Preston, C.D. (1989). The spread of *Epilobium ciliatum* Raf. in the British Isles. *Watsonia* **17**: 279–288.

Preston, C.D. & Croft, J.M. (1997). *Aquatic plants in Britain and Ireland.* Harley Books, Colchester.

Preston, C.D. & Hill, M.O. (1997). The geographical relationships of British and Irish vascular plants. *Botanical Journal of the Linnean Society* **124**: 1–120.

Preston, C.D. & Hill, M.O. (1999). The geographical relationships of the British and Irish flora: a comparison of pteridophytes, flowering plants, liverworts and mosses. *Journal of Biogeography* **26**: 629–642.

Preston, C.D., Hollingsworth, P.M. & Gornall, R.J. (1999). The distribution and habitat of *Potamogeton* × *suecicus* K. Richt. (*P. filiformis* Pers. × *P. pectinatus* L.) in the British Isles. *Watsonia* **22**: 329–342.

Preston, C.D., Roy, D.B. & Hill, M.O. (1997). The phytogeography of Scotland. *Botanical Journal of Scotland* **49**: 191–204.

Preston, C.D., Stewart, N.F. & Palmer, M.A. (in press.) The standing waters of Coll and Tiree in a national and international context. *Botanical Journal of Scotland* **52**.

Pugsley, H.W. (1930). A revision of the British Euphrasiae. *Journal of the Linnean Society of London (Botany)* **48**: 467–544.

Pugsley, H.W. (1948). A prodromus of the British Hieracia. *Journal of the Linnean Society of London (Botany)* **54**: 1–356.

Raven, J.E. (1949). Alien plant introductions on the Isle of Rhum. *Nature* **163**: 104–105.

Richardson, J.A. (1970). John William Heslop-Harrison (1881–1967). *Watsonia* **8**: 181–182.

Ritchie, W. (1976). The meaning and definition of machair. *Transactions of the Botanical Society of Edinburgh* **42**: 431–440.

Rodwell, J.S., ed. (1991–1995). *British plant communities*, **1–4**. Cambridge University Press, Cambridge.

Rodwell, J.S., ed. (in press). *British plant communities*, **5**. Cambridge University Press, Cambridge.

Sabbagh, K. (1999). *A Rum Affair*. Allen Lane, London.

Scott, T. (1881). Notes, chiefly botanical, of a visit to the island of Coll. *Proceedings of the Natural History Society of Glasgow* 4: 226–230.

Sell, P.D. (1998). *Pilosella*. In Rich, T.C.G. & Jermy, A.C., *Plant Crib 1998*, pp. 297–299. Botanical Society of the British Isles, London.

Sell, P.D. & Murrell, G. (1996). *Flora of Great Britain and Ireland*. 5, *Butomaceae–Orchidaceae*. Cambridge University Press, Cambridge.

Shepherd, K.B. (1989). Breeding wader distribution, ecology and numbers. In Stroud, D.A., ed. *Birds on Coll and Tiree: status, habitats and conservation*, pp. 25–41. Nature Conservancy Council & Scottish Ornithologists' Club, Edinburgh.

Stace, C.A. (1991). *New Flora of the British Isles*. Cambridge University Press, Cambridge.

Stace, C.A. (1997). *New Flora of the British Isles*, ed. 2. Cambridge University Press, Cambridge.

Stace, C.A., Styles, B.T. & Timson, J. (1975). *Polygonum* L. In Stace, C.A., ed. *Hybridization and the flora of the British Isles*, pp. 273–277. Academic Press, London.

Stewart, A., Pearman, D.A. & Preston, C.D., comps & eds (1994). *Scarce plants in Britain*. Joint Nature Conservation Committee, Peterborough.

Stewart, N.F. (1996). Stoneworts – connoisseurs of clean water. *British Wildlife* 8: 92–99.

Stewart, N.F. & Church, J.M. (1992). *Red Data Books of Britain and Ireland: Stoneworts*. Joint Nature Conservation Committee, Peterborough.

Stewart, N.F. & Preston, C.D. (in press). The stoneworts of Coll and Tiree. *Botanical Journal of Scotland* 52.

Stroud, D.A., ed. (1989). *Birds on Coll and Tiree: status, habitats and conservation*. Nature Conservancy Council & Scottish Ornithologists' Club, Edinburgh.

Taylor, G. (1959). John Walker, D.D., F.R.S.E., 1731–1803. A notable Scottish botanist. *Transactions of the Botanical Society of Edinburgh* 38: 180–203.

Vose, P.B., Powell, H.G. & Spence, J.B. (1957). The machair grazings of Tiree, Inner Hebrides. *Transactions of the Botanical Society of Edinburgh* 37: 89–110.

Wallace, E.C., comp. (1953). Plant records. *Watsonia* 2: 335–358.

Wallace, E.C., comp. (1954). Plant records. *Proceedings of the Botanical Society of the British Isles* 1: 41–69.

Wigginton, M.J., comp. & ed. (1999). *British Red Data Books 1 Vascular plants*, ed. 3. Joint Nature Conservation Committee, Peterborough.

Wilmott, A.J. (1944). Vice-counties. *Report of the Botanical Society and Exchange Club of the British Isles* 12: 524–526.

Withrington, D.J. & Grant, I.R., eds (1983). *The statistical account of Scotland 1791–1799 edited by Sir John Sinclair*, 20. *The Western Isles (of Ross, Inverness-shire and Argyll, with Bute)*. EP Publishing, Wakefield.

Wormell, P. (1989). Bird habitats on Coll and Tiree. In Stroud, D.A., ed. *Birds on Coll and Tiree: status, habitats and conservation*, pp. 9–17. Nature Conservancy Council & Scottish Ornithologists' Club, Edinburgh.

Mentha aquatica × *spicata (M. × piperita)* "Found once near Balephuil", T 94, a second locality from the island.

Mentha spicata × **suaveolens (M. × villosa)** By sandy stream running into Vaul Bay, T 04. Only otherwise known from one site in W Tiree.

[*Platanthera chlorantha* Recorded as "abundant on Coll in 1947" in the 1951 paper, with a note that "it swarmed similarly in 1949 in the Loch Iasgair area of South Uist". There are no other records from Coll and we are reluctant to accept this unlocalised report though the species occurs elsewhere in the Inner Hebrides.]

Pyrola media Carnan Mora, C 25, 1947, a second colony of this species.

Pyrola minor "When we revisited Coll in 1947 we discovered that the only known colony of *P. minor* had been burnt off". There have been no records since.

?**Quercus petraea** Recorded in the 1951 paper from three additional sites, the shores of Loch an Duin, C 25, the cliffs above Loch a'Mhill Aird and Loch na Cloiche, C 26.

[**Rosa canina** Recorded as var. *biserrata* from Balephetrish Hill, T 04. We are reluctant to accept this as a record of *R. canina*, which has not been confirmed from Tiree.]

Veronica catenata "On a stream running into Vaul Bay, Tiree", T 04. The only other record is from W Coll.

Veronica persica Not recorded by HH, but reported in the 1951 paper from cultivated ground at the base of An Cnap, Tiree, T 04.

Vicia orobus "On rocks, west of Totronald, Isle of Coll", C 15. Never reported again, but found on Mull, Ardnamurchan, Rum and Skye.

Heslop Harrison, J.W. (1951). Further observations on the vascular plants of the Outer and Inner Hebrides. *Transactions of the Botanical Society of Edinburgh* **35**: 415-426.

D. A. Pearman & C. D. Preston, March 2000

FLORA OF TIREE, GUNNA AND COLL

ADDENDUM

Within a day of our Flora going to the printer, we came across a significant paper by J.W. Heslop Harrison (1951) which we had overlooked. It contains records made on Tiree and Coll in 1947 (the year that his son, J. Heslop Harrison, visited the islands to study *Dactylorhiza*). Although Heslop Harrison's paper is published in a mainstream journal, these records have also been overlooked in other publications so we are including them in an addendum distributed with the Flora. They include three species which were not included at all in our Flora, *Juncus tenuis*, *Platanthera chlorantha* and *Vicia orobus*, and two taxa not recorded from Tiree, *Dactylorhiza incarnata × purpurella* and *Veronica catenata*. Heslop Harrison's comments on the effect of fires on *Betula pubescens* and *Pyrola minor* are also interesting. Such fires continue to occur (Mrs P. Braithwaite remembers an especially severe one in the Loch Fada area before 1983 whose effects remained visible for many years) and they obviously contribute to the scarcity of trees on this part of the island.

This addendum also gives us the opportunity to acknowledge with thanks a grant from RSPB towards the cost of the cover of the Flora.

Betula pubescens In the 1951 paper Heslop Harrison reported that the 'little birch copse along Loch Cliad [C 15] has been destroyed by post-war moorland firing' but he recorded additional trees from Ben Hogh, C 15, and the Druim Fishaig cliffs, C 26.

*Carduus crispus Area between Ruaig and Miodar, T 04, a second locality on Tiree.

Dactylorhiza incarnata × purpurella (D. × latirella) Ceann a'Mhara, Tiree, T 94.

[***Fumaria officinalis*** "By a *lapsus calami*, this species, occurring rarely in fields in the west of Coll, was listed as *F. purpurea* in the Coll Flora". In fact, HH in his Flora recorded *F. purpurea* from Torastan, in NE Coll. The record of *F. purpurea*, which we treated as doubtful, must therefore be regarded as an error; we are also unwilling to accept the records of *F. officinalis* in the absence of voucher specimens.]

*Juncus tenuis "Found on a bare patch of ground behind a wall near Loch Caol, Tiree; new to v.c. 103." This report from T 04 is the only record of a species which can be expected to occur as an alien on the islands.

INDEX